DEBBIE MATTHEW.
SOUTHAMPTON.

FIONA McKENZIE.
ABERDEENSHIRE.

ELLA DAVIS.
LONDON.

HELEN ADAMS.
WOLVERHAMPTON.

JULIA TURNER.
NORFOLK.

MARGARET GLEESON,
HAMPSHIRE.

65p

ANNUAL '76

FUN

THINGS TO MAKE

PICTURES

POP

GAMES

Features

STORIES

COLOUR

FUN for ALL

85 Fleet Street, London, EC4A 2HS., © D. C. THOMSON & CO., LTD., 1975.

THE BABY SITTERS

HESTER and Honey were two sisters who ran a baby-sitting agency. Everyone agreed that they certainly had a way with children.

One evening, at home—

YOUR HAIR HAS TAKEN AGES TO DRY, HONEY. I DON'T KNOW WHY YOU DIDN'T USE THE HAIRDRYER. IT'S QUICK AND EFFICIENT.

I PREFER TO DRY MY HAIR THE OLD-FASHIONED WAY—NATURALLY. ANYWAY, EFFICIENT MODERN GADGETS—

—SEEM TO HAVE A HABIT OF BREAKING DOWN!

The girls were due to baby-sit at Mrs Fodor's at eight o'clock.

WE'D BETTER HURRY UP! IT'S AFTER EIGHT! TRUST THAT BUS TO BREAK DOWN!

THAT'S UP-TO-DATE MACHINERY EFFICIENCY FOR YOU—AND NOW MY WATCH HAS STOPPED!

After the girls had seen Mrs Fodor off—

MRS FODOR SAID WE WERE TO MAKE OURSELVES AT HOME— BUT HOW? THIS HOUSE IS SO UP-TO-DATE THERE'S NOTHING IN IT!

PERHAPS WE'RE SUPPOSED TO SIT ON THE FLOOR! LET'S SEE WHAT THE REST OF THE HOUSE IS LIKE.

Tara wanted a glass of milk, so she led the way to the kitchen.

But Honey had thought wrongly!

OOH! OUCH!

As Honey was pitched into the sink, Hester and Tara came to find out the cause of the noise.

HAVING A NICE DIP, HONEY?

Later—

THERE'S NOTHING WRONG WITH MODERN EFFICIENCY—IF YOU KNOW HOW TO HANDLE IT PROPERLY!

WELL, I HOPE YOU HAVE A MODERN, EFFICIENT CURE FOR THE OLD-FASHIONED COLD I GOT FROM BEING SOAKED BY MODERN GADGETRY!

Fun at the Fair

S UE AND LINDA go to the fair and find more than they thought they would—puzzles galore on every fairground stall. Go round the sideshows with Sue and Linda and try to solve the puzzles. If you get stuck, or want to check your answers, the solutions are at the foot of the opposite page.

1

These two swing-boats look identical until you look more closely. There are six differences between them. Can you spot them?

2

These laughing clowns all look alike, don't they? However, if you look more closely, you will see that only two are identical. Which two?

3

How many goldfish do you see in this tank?

4

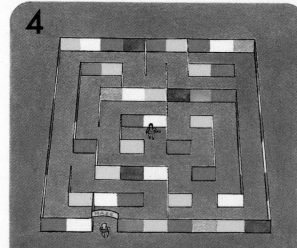

Linda went into the maze, but Sue decided not to go. Now Linda is lost. Can you lead her out to Sue?

5

CEEFFO * AET * ADEELMNO

CEI-ACEMR

ACDNY SSLFO

EEFFOT AELPPS * EESSTW

OHTODGS ABEGHMRRSU

TAOOPT CIPRSS

Can you help our two chums to unscramble the names of the snacks advertised on the caravan?

6

Hidden in this picture are 10 small articles. Can you spot them?

7

Can you solve the word square on this target?

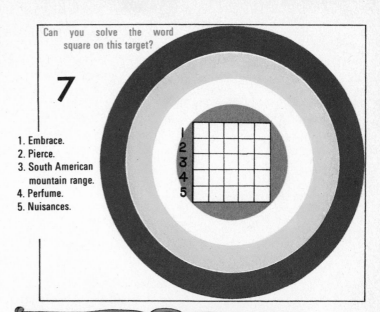

1. Embrace.
2. Pierce.
3. South American mountain range.
4. Perfume.
5. Nuisances.

9

Another problem for Sue and Linda—how many prizes on this stall begin with the letter "T"?

8

How observant are you? Sue and Linda have met two friends and our artist has drawn them again. But he has included at least eight mistakes in this picture. What are they?

10

Here is a last look at the fair, with Sue and Linda waving goodbye. Colour it for yourself with your crayons and see how bright and attractive you can make it.

1. FIRST, YOU WILL NEED A PIECE OF THIN CARDBOARD, AT LEAST 10" SQUARE. A LARGE CEREAL PACKET, OPENED OUT, WOULD BE IDEAL.
DRAW A CIRCLE, 9" ACROSS, THEN ANOTHER, WITHIN IT, OF 6" ACROSS, USING THE SAME CENTRE POINT.
THEN MARK OFF 55 HALF-INCH POINTS ROUND THE OUTER CIRCLE, (SEE ABOVE). THESE POINTS DO NOT NEED TO BE EXACTLY SPACED, BUT YOU MUST FINISH UP WITH AN ODD NUMBER OF POINTS.

2. LAY A RULER FROM EACH POINT TO THE CENTRE, AND RULE LINES BETWEEN THE TWO CIRCLES. THEN, USING A KNITTING NEEDLE, OR SOMETHING SIMILAR, POKE A HOLE AT BOTH ENDS OF EACH LINE.

3. SEW A CURTAIN RING LOOSELY IN THE CENTRE OF THE CIRCLES.

THREAD   CURTAIN RING

make a top-pop tammy !

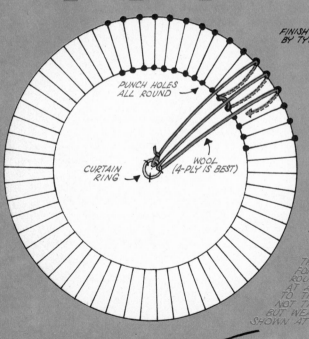

PUNCH HOLES ALL ROUND

CURTAIN RING   WOOL (4-PLY IS BEST)

FINISH OFF BY TYING

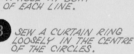

A

B

4. NOW YOUR CARD SHOULD LOOK LIKE THE LARGE PICTURE AT THE LEFT. THREAD THE 'WARP' BY FIRST TYING WOOL TO THE CENTRE RING AND CONTINUING AS SHOWN. ON COMPLETION, YOUR CARD WILL LOOK LIKE 'A' ABOVE ON ONE SIDE, AND LIKE 'B' ON THE OTHER.

THREAD A BODKIN WITH WOOL FOR THE WEAVING, USING ROUGHLY TWO-FOOT LENGTHS AT A TIME. WHEN YOU COME TO THE END OF A LENGTH, DO NOT TIE ON THE NEXT LENGTH BUT WEAVE IT ALONGSIDE AS SHOWN AT THE BOTTOM LEFT.

STARTING AT THE CURTAIN RING, WEAVE THE CENTRE SECTION IN COLOUR OR BLACK TO ABOUT 3" ACROSS, THEN WEAVE A WHITE BAND 1/2" WIDE. CONTINUE IN ALTERNATE 1/2" BANDS OF COLOUR/WHITE UNTIL THE OUTER EDGE IS REACHED. THEN EMBROIDER THE NAME OF YOUR FAVOURITE POP-STAR OR GROUP IN THE CENTRE. TURN YOUR BOARD OVER AND WEAVE FROM THE HEADBAND, STARTING WITH COLOUR, ONE WHITE BAND, FINISHING WITH COLOUR. JUST TEAR OUT THE CARDBOARD AND YOUR 'TOP-POP TAMMY' IS COMPLETE!

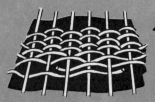

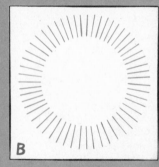

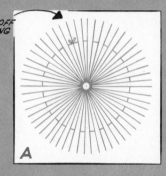

IT'S A HIT!

How fast can you make it to the top? Try this game and find out! You need a dice, and each player has a counter. Throw a 6 to start, and then you're off. Remember, when you're nearing the top, you must throw the exact number to finish! Good luck!

START HERE

Miss bus to folk club
MISS A TURN

You arrive late
MOVE ON 3

Mike breaks down
MOVE BACK 2

Spotted by talent scout
MOVE ON 1

DISCOVERED

Signed up to make record

You're in the wrong studio
MOVE BACK 1

Broken string
MISS A TURN

Start to sing

Voice sounds flat
MOVE BACK 1

Disc made on 3rd attempt

No holes in discs
MISS 2 TURNS

Records sent to Hong Kong by mistake
MOVE BACK 2

Played on radio 1
MOVE ON 2

NO 4

Doing well
MOVE ON 1

TIP FOR THE TOP!

Asked to appear on T V

SCREAM SCREAM

Kept awake by screaming fans
MISS A TURN

ZOO

Taken to zoo instead of T V studio
MOVE BACK 2

T V appearance is a fab success!

NO. 1

You're top of the charts!

HOORAY!

HOORAY!

World-famous! You've made it!

YOU CAN TURN YOUR RECORD-PLAYER INTO A SUPER DRAWING INSTRUMENT IN A FEW MINUTES! IT WILL NOT HARM IT AND WILL GIVE YOU HOURS OF FUN!

FIRST, CUT A DISC OF (PREFERABLY) CORRUGATED CARD, 5" IN DIAMETER, MAKING A CENTRAL HOLE SLIGHTLY LARGER THAN THE CENTRAL PILLAR.

STICKY TAPE

5"

THEN, CUT A DISC OF WHITE PAPER TO FIT, AND FASTEN THE DISCS AS SHOWN ABOVE.

your own
design factory !

USE FELT PENS OR PAINTING STICKS. DO **NOT** TRY BALL-POINTS OR CRAYONS ETC. AS TOO MUCH PRESSURE WOULD BE NEEDED.

78
45
33

SET THE SPEED TO 45 R.P.M. AND LIGHTLY DRAW A FELT PEN FROM THE OUTSIDE OF THE DISC TO ITS CENTRE. RESULT— A PERFECT SPIRAL!

IF YOU CONTINUE RIGHT ACROSS THE DISC, IT WILL DRAW A SECOND SPIRAL IN THE OPPOSITE DIRECTION. TRY DIFFERENT COLOURS.

TWO PENS HELD TOGETHER AND MOVED FASTER, WILL PRODUCE THIS DESIGN.

DO IT SEVERAL TIMES, IN VARIOUS COLOURS, AND YOU PRODUCE THE ABOVE. THEN TAKE THE DISC OFF AND COLOUR THE SPACES.

A
B

© D

A MORE ADVANCED TYPE OF DESIGN CAN BE MADE AS FOLLOWS.

PROVIDED YOUR PLAYER HAS A TALL CENTRAL PILLAR, STEADY YOUR HAND AGAINST IT AS IN Ⓐ

THEN JUST SCRIBBLE BETWEEN FINGER AND THUMB AS IN Ⓑ

THIS WILL PRODUCE DESIGNS LIKE © AND Ⓓ

REGULAR CIRCLES ARE MADE JUST BY HOLDING THE PEN STILL AT ONE POINT.

DON'T TRY TO IMITATE OUR OWN DESIGNS EXACTLY. JUST SCRIBBLE ON THE DISC AND ALLOW THE CIRCULAR MOTION TO DO THE REST. EXPERIMENT WITH VARIOUS COLOURS AND DRAWING AT DIFFERENT SPEEDS. STUCK ON TO HARDBOARD AND COVERED WITH PLASTIC, THE DISCS WILL MAKE EXCELLENT TABLE MATS. DECORATE GIFT-BOXES — A FRIEZE FOR YOUR BEDROOM — YOU'LL FIND LOTS OF USES FOR YOUR DESIGNS!

TIDY HEADS

"A place for everything and everything in its place"—that's a motto you'll all love to practise when you've completed our easy-to-make "Tidy Heads".

You will need—
ONE LARGE PACKET OF PLASTER OF PARIS (for two heads), TWO EMPTY TINS, FINE EMERY PAPER, POSTER PAINTS AND PAINTBRUSH, NEWSPAPER, CLEAR LACQUER SPRAY, SPATULA, KNIFE, RUBBER GLOVES, DOLLS' GLASS EYES.

1—Mix some plaster of Paris and water into a thin paste, then knead half pages of newspaper into it. 2—Squeeze out the water, place the mixture onto a wooden base and push in the tin, covering the sides but leaving the top open. Leave overnight to dry. 3—Next day, use more plaster of Paris and water to make a thick paste, and, using the spatula, add the paste to the hardened mixture around the tin to form a rough head and neck shape. Make a small nose, smooth over the paste and leave for an hour to dry. 4—Now, using the kitchen knife, scrape the surface until it's perfectly smooth, starting at the top and working down until both sides are symmetrical. Then cover the head with a thin layer of paste and, when dry, rub lightly with emery paper.

1 MIX PASTE

2 PLACE TUBE

3 ROUGH SHAPE

4 FORM NOSE AND SAND SMOOTH

5 PAINT AND VARNISH

5—Next, mark out the eye holes and secure the eyes in their 'sockets' with paste. Smooth over the excess paste surrounding the eyes. Now, using a wide paintbrush and a flesh colour, mixed with lots of white, apply the complexion. When this has dried, use black paint to apply the hair and moustache as shown. Leave to dry, then spray with lacquer.
To complete your Tidy Head, paint on a bow tie in whatever colour you wish, but remember to spray with lacquer for a good finished surface.

Apart from having a useful purpose, your Tidy Heads will brighten up any room or make a gift your friends would be thrilled to receive!

IT'S ONE OF THOSE DAYS

How often have you said that? Often enough, I'm sure. Have you ever wondered why we have "off-days" when nothing seems to go right and days when everything goes like clockwork? Well, many scientists believe it's because our lives are influenced by three cycles—a PHYSICAL one, lasting 23 days, an EMOTIONAL one, lasting 28 days and an INTELLECTUAL one, lasting 33 days. These cycles have been called "bio rhythmics", and, since each rhythm occurs within a predictable cycle, it has been discovered that they can actually be plotted on a graph which will reveal the basic pattern of your life for any future week, month or year!

Below, with the aid of an example, there are step by step instructions on how to prepare your own bio rhythm graph for the month of January, 1976.

Our example birthday is August 6th, 1963.

STAGE 1

Work out the number of days you have lived, from the day of your birth to the first day of January. To do this, first multiply 365 (the number of days in a year) by your age. When you have reached this figure—(a) add 1 day for every leap year since your birthday; (b) add the number of days between your last birthday and the 1st January. Looking at our example, we see the subject was 12 years of age on the 6th August, 1975. Thus, to work out the number of days the subject has lived until January 1st, 1976, our calculations on paper would appear like this—

$$
\begin{array}{ll}
& 365 \text{ days} \\
\times & 12 \text{ years} \\
\hline
= & 4380 \text{ days} \\
\text{add} & 3 \text{ days for leap years} \\
\hline
= & 4383 \text{ days} \\
\text{add} & 147 \text{ days from 6th August,} \\
& \quad 1975 \text{ to 1st Jan. 1976} \\
\hline
= & 4530 \text{ days total}
\end{array}
$$

STAGE 2

The next step is to calculate the PHYSICAL, EMOTIONAL and INTELLECTUAL cycles which have taken place since birth. These are arrived at by dividing the total days of stage 1 by 3 figures—

23 for the PHYSICAL cycle
28 for the EMOTIONAL cycle
33 for the INTELLECTUAL cycle

So, continuing our example calculations—

$4530 \div 23 = 196$ complete cycles and 22 days
$4530 \div 28 = 161$ complete cycles and 22 days
$4530 \div 33 = 137$ complete cycles and 9 days

Note that in each case there is no exact division. In fact, the remaining number of days are the essential numbers needed to plot the graph.

STAGE 3

To draw the graph, ideally, graph paper should be used, but plain paper divided into graph format will do. Draw your basic graph shape as we've shown, dividing it off into equally spaced lines to represent the 31 days of January. The line running along the middle of the graph is called the "O" datum line. The section above this line is the positive half and the section below the line is the negative half. All this will be explained in more detail later.

Now the calculations of Stage 2 must be transferred to the graph chart. Although this step may appear a little complicated, if the instructions are carried out carefully, you should have no trouble in completing your graph. To avoid confusion, the three cycles have been drawn in different colours. PHYSICAL—RED. EMOTIONAL—BLUE. INTELLECTUAL—GREEN.

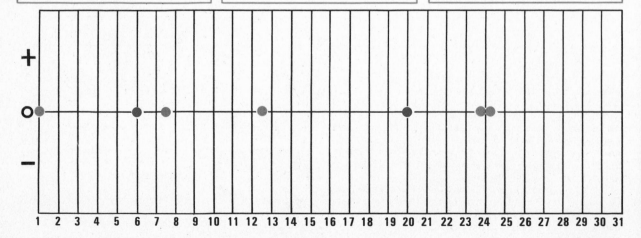

PHYSICAL RHYTHM
23 DAYS CYCLE

Referring to our Stage 2 calculations, we see that our test subject is 22 days into a new physical cycle on January 1st, 1976. Since 22 is greater than the half-cycle—11½ days, the physical rhythm line must start in the NEGATIVE half of the chart. If your own particular number is less than the half-cycle, then your physical rhythm line will start in the POSITIVE half of the chart. The most important days to be plotted are the points where the rhythm line crosses the "0" datum line. In our example, the first of these cross-over points is reached at by taking January 1st as day 23. Since a physical cycle is 23 days long, a new physical cycle is completed for the subject on the first day of January. Thus, the first red dot is placed on the datum line at January 1st. The rest of the datum line points come at 11½ day intervals. In our example, you'll see these are the 12th, 13th and 24th.

EMOTIONAL RHYTHM
28 DAYS CYCLE

This rhythm is worked out in the same way as the physical one. In this case, the half-cycle is 14 days and since our subject's remaining number of days is 22 and therefore greater than the half-cycle, the emotional rhythm starts in the negative half of the chart. Our subject is 22 days into a new emotional cycle on January 1st. So, by taking 1st January as day 23, we count along the datum line until the 28th day—a complete emotional cycle—is reached. Thus the complete cycle is reached on January 6th and a corresponding blue dot is placed on the datum line. The rest of the datum line points come at 14 day intervals. In our example, there is only one other—on the 20th.

INTELLECTUAL RHYTHM
33 DAYS CYCLE

Our subject is 9 days into a new intellectual cycle on January 1st. This number is less than the half-cycle—16½ days—so the intellectual rhythm begins in the positive half of the chart. Taking January 1st as day 10 and counting along the datum line until the 33rd day is reached, you'll see the first datum line point lands on the 24th January—also shared with the physical cycle. The remaining points are at 16½ day intervals—in this case—7th and 8th.

STAGE 4

Now that the datum line points of the three rhythms have been plotted, they must be interconnected by a cyclic line. These lines form symmetrical curves from point to point. Thus, our subject's completed graph looks like this—

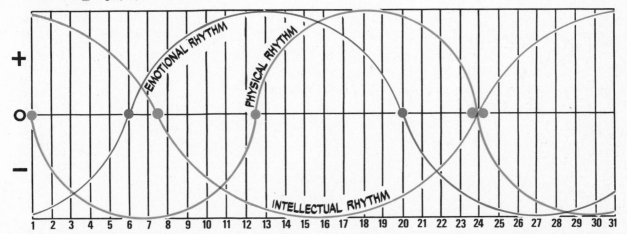

On every bio rhythm chart, the curves are exactly the same shape except that they cut the datum line at different places. To help you draw the curves on your graph, cover our completed example with a piece of tracing paper, and, with the appropriate coloured pencil, trace each of the three curves. When you have done this, simply transfer the tracing paper to your graph and then copy the curve lines, relative to where your datum line points are plotted.

Basically, the graph indicates when the subject will be at her peak and at her lowest point, physically, emotionally and intellectually during the month of January. You can see a physical peak is reached on

the 18th and a low on the 7th. Emotionally, a peak falls on the 13th and a low on the 27th. The 31st is an intellectual peak and the 16th a low. When the curves cross the "0" datum line, these are important as being transition periods between the negative and positive sections of the chart. Scientists believe that people are more prone to "off-days" during these times and if two curves cross the datum line at exactly the same point, as in our example, then a very "off-day" is indicated!

You can draw a bio rhythm chart for any month you like. Now that we've shown you how to do it—see how much of what it reveals comes true!

Jill reported for duty.

YOU SHOULDN'T HAVE ANY PROBLEMS. ALL THE PATIENTS IN THIS WARD ARE WELL ON THE WAY TO RECOVERY. WELL, I'M OFF TO BED. GOOD NIGHT.

GOOD NIGHT.

All was quiet for a time. Then—

I SMELL SMOKE! OH, THERE'S THE FIRE ALARM! GET UP, EVERYBODY!

THE FIRE'S COMING UP THE LIFT SHAFT! WE CAN'T USE THE LIFT OR THE STAIRS! WE'RE TRAPPED!

TURN BACK! THERE MAY BE ANOTHER STAIRCASE!

I ONLY HOPE THERE IS! BUT I HAVEN'T BEEN HERE LONG ENOUGH TO KNOW THE BUILDING PROPERLY.

SOMEONE'S BECKONING TO US! IT'S THE GIRL I SAW IN MY MIRROR!

SHE'S LED US TO A PASSAGEWAY THAT I DIDN'T EVEN KNOW EXISTED. COME ON, EVERYBODY, WE'RE ALL RIGHT NOW!

WELL DONE, NURSE! THAT'S EVERYBODY ACCOUNTED FOR! I'M GLAD YOU KEPT YOUR HEAD.

ONE OF THE OTHER NURSES GUIDED ME, MATRON. SHE WAS AHEAD OF US, BUT I CAN'T SEE HER NOW.

THAT'S STRANGE. I SAW NOBODY COME OUT AHEAD OF YOU. AND ALL THE OTHER NURSES WERE BUSY CARING FOR THEIR OWN PATIENTS.

BUT WE WERE GUIDED OUT BY A NURSE! AND I THINK I KNOW NOW WHO IT WAS—ANN PAXLEY!

JILL NEVER SAW THE NURSE AGAIN. WAS IT REALLY ANN PAXLEY, RETURNED BECAUSE SHE WAS NEEDED AGAIN? JILL WILL ALWAYS BE CONVINCED OF IT. WHAT DO YOU THINK?

3-D FLOWER PICTURES

SO EASY TO MAKE!

HERE'S A WONDERFUL NEW HOBBY FOR YOU TO TRY. SAVE METAL FOIL PAPER, SILVER AND COLOURED, FROM CHOCOLATE BARS ETC. THEN TRACE OUT THE SEPARATE SHAPES OF EACH FLOWER ONTO CARD AND CUT OUT

THE COLOURS SHOWN ARE ONLY SUGGESTIONS. DON'T WORRY IF YOU HAVEN'T THE SAME COLOURS. YOU CAN STILL MAKE WONDERFUL FLOWERS.

WRAP EACH CARD SHAPE ROUND WITH FOIL PAPER, PRESSING FIRST INTO PLACE WITH YOUR FINGERS . . .

. . . THEN BURNISHING DOWN SMOOTHLY WITH A SPOON HANDLE

THE FOIL NEED NOT COVER THE BACK COMPLETELY.

A BLACK BACKGROUND IS MOST STRIKING FOR YOUR FLOWERS. USE BLACK CARTRIDGE PAPER OR — BETTER STILL — BLACK MATERIAL GUMMED TO A SHEET OF CARD. VELVET GIVES A PARTICULARLY RICH EFFECT!

GLUE EACH PIECE LIGHTLY INTO PLACE, LEAVING GAPS AS IN THE BIG PICTURES. DON'T TRY TO COPY THE GAP SIZES EXACTLY. YOU'LL BE SURPRISED HOW EASILY YOU CAN PUT THE FLOWERS TOGETHER AND WHAT A SUPER EFFECT THEY WILL GIVE!

ONCE YOU GET THE IDEA, YOU CAN USE THE SAME METHOD FOR OTHER SUBJECTS — BOATS, CRINOLINE LADIES, BIRDS — A WONDERFUL NEW HOBBY THAT COSTS PRACTICALLY NOTHING!

MARY MARCH, the eldest girl at the Moorlands Children's Home, was a great help to matron, Miss Barlow. One afternoon when matron was away for a few hours, Mary was left in charge.

MARY OF MOORLANDS

WE'RE OFF TO THE BATHS NOW, MARY. WHAT TIME WILL TEA BE?

AROUND HALF-PAST FOUR. I'M TAKING THE OTHERS TO THE PARK, AND WE'LL HAVE TEA THERE. BYE; ENJOY YOURSELVES.

DAVID LOOKS SAD. POOR KID—I EXPECT HE'S WISHING HE COULD GO SWIMMING, TOO.

David had a weak heart, and was not allowed strenuous exercise.

WHEN WE GET TO THE PARK, WE'LL GO TO THE BOATING-POND. I'LL TREAT YOU TO A TRIP IN ONE OF THOSE LITTLE MOTOR BOATS. WOULD YOU LIKE THAT?

YES, PLEASE!

THE OTHER KIDS WON'T BE JEALOUS. DAVID IS SORT OF SPECIAL TO ALL OF US, BECAUSE HE'S NOT STRONG.

THANKS, MARY!

The treat brought a sparkle to David's eyes.

HE'LL ONLY GET TEN MINUTES FOR TENPENCE, BUT IT'S WORTH IT, BECAUSE HE'S ENJOYING HIMSELF SO MUCH.

Afterwards, in the playground, David wanted on the climbing frame.

I'LL TAKE IT SLOWLY, I PROMISE.

ALL RIGHT THEN, DAVID. SHALL I HOLD YOUR RADIO FOR YOU?

NO, THANKS. I CAN MANAGE.

HE HATES TO BE PARTED FROM HIS RADIO. IT'S VERY SPECIAL TO HIM, BECAUSE HIS MUM AND DAD GAVE IT TO HIM JUST BEFORE THEY WERE KILLED IN THAT ROAD ACCIDENT.

David was near the top of the climbing-frame, when he missed his footing.

HOLD ON, DAVID! I'M COMING!

But David tried to swing back up, and lost hold of his radio.

MY RADIO!

IT'S SMASHED! POOR DAVID, HE'LL BE HEARTBROKEN!

Mary got David safely down.

I'VE GATHERED UP ALL THE BITS, MARY. I EXPECT DAVID WILL WANT TO KEEP THEM.

THANKS, PAT. I THINK WE'D BETTER GO HOME, KIDS. WE CAN HAVE THE PICNIC IN THE GARDEN.

David was so upset that Mary got him to bed and sent for the doctor.

HE'S TO TAKE TWO OF THESE EVERY SIX HOURS, MARY. TELL MATRON I'LL CALL AGAIN TOMORROW. HE'LL NEED A FEW DAYS IN BED.

HE'LL NEED A LOT OF LOVE AND UNDER-STANDING, TOO.

A week later, David was still in bed.

DAVID, YOU MUST EAT. COME ON, HAVE A TRY, TO PLEASE ME.

I'M NOT HUNGRY. GO AWAY, MARY. I DON'T WANT TO TALK. I WANT TO BE ON MY OWN.

Mary reported to matron.

POOR LAD! I WISH WE COULD FIND A WAY TO CHEER HIM UP.

PERHAPS ANOTHER SPECIAL RADIO WOULD HELP. I'LL HAVE A TALK WITH THE OTHER KIDS ABOUT IT.

They agreed to buy David a new radio, and emptied their money boxes.

LOOKS LIKE WE'VE GOT ENOUGH FOR A CHEAP ONE. STILL, DAVID'S BROKEN ONE WASN'T POSH.

BUT IT WAS SPECIAL, AND PERHAPS OUR USING OUR SAVINGS TO BUY A RADIO FOR HIM WILL MAKE IT SPECIAL FOR DAVID, TOO.

But when David was given the new radio—

I DON'T WANT ANOTHER RADIO! I-I'M SORRY, B-BUT I JUST DON'T WANT IT!

TH-THIS ONE MADE ME FEEL MY MUM AND DAD WERE WITH ME, SORT OF. I-I—

WE UNDERSTAND, DAVID. WE WON'T TAKE OFFENCE. DON'T CRY.

I WANT MY MUM! I WANT HER!

POOR LITTLE KID! OH, HOW I WISH I HADN'T LET HIM GO UP THAT CLIMBING-FRAME.

MAYBE WE COULD SELL THE RADIO, MARY, AND BUY DAVID SOMETHING ELSE WITH THE MONEY.

LIKE A MODEL AIRCRAFT KIT. HE LIKES MAKING MODELS, AND HE'S GOOD AT IT.

I DON'T THINK THAT WOULD HELP, BOYS. STILL, I WILL SEE IF THE SHOP WILL TAKE THE RADIO BACK.

Mary had bought it at a small, local shop.

I EXPECT MR HARRIS IS IN HIS WORKSHOP. HE WON'T MIND MY GOING THROUGH. HE'S A NICE MAN, AND VERY KIND.

Mr Harris willingly refunded the money Mary had paid for the radio.

AND THERE'S AN EXTRA POUND. BUY DAVID SOMETHING NICE WITH IT.

THANKS, MR HARRIS! GOSH, THAT'S A POSH RADIO YOU'RE WORKING ON. IT LOOKS VERY COMPLICATED.

POSH? WHY, NO. IT'S ONE I'M MAKING MYSELF, MARY, FROM BITS AND PIECES OF BROKEN-DOWN RADIOS.

THAT GIVES ME AN IDEA!

That afternoon—

YOU NEED SOME FRESH AIR. THE DOCTOR SAYS SO. WE'LL JUST GO AS FAR AS MR HARRIS'S SHOP. HE WANTS TO TALK TO YOU.

BUT I DON'T WANT TO GET UP, MARY. I DON'T WANT TO GO FOR A WALK.

A little later—

ME MAKE A RADIO? I WOULDN'T KNOW HOW. ANYWAY, I-I CAN'T BE BOTHERED.

IT WOULD BE SPECIAL, IF YOU MADE IT YOURSELF, DAVID, BECAUSE OF ALL THE EFFORT YOU'D PUT IN.

I'D HELP YOU, DAVID. I'VE GOT ENOUGH KNOW-HOW FOR THE TWO OF US.

DON'T TOUCH!

I WAS JUST LOOKING TO SEE IF THERE'RE SOME BITS WE COULD USE, IF YOU DECIDE TO MAKE A RADIO.

THAT SHOULD SELL MY IDEA TO DAVID.

Mr Harris found two small parts that could be used.

OH, MARY! IN A WAY, I'LL HAVE MY SPECIAL RADIO BACK, BECAUSE THOSE TWO PARTS WILL BE HELPING TO MAKE THE NEW RADIO WORK.

SO THEY WILL.

A few days later—

I'VE GOT TO BE BACK AT MR HARRIS'S IN AN HOUR, MARY, TO DO SOME MORE WORK ON MY RADIO. GOSH, THE DINNER SMELLS GOOD! I'M HUNGRY!

AND HAPPY AGAIN, TOO, THANK GOODNESS!

BUTTON UP!

Every house has its "button box"—a treasure trove of colourful odds and ends that have been gathered over the years. Here are a few interesting ways for you to try mounting and displaying them.

By using pieces of coloured felt along with your buttons, such designs as a plant, a peacock, a tree, a clown and a sunset can be made. Try out simple designs before attempting anything elaborate. Always sketch your ideas out first with pencil or chalk before putting needle to cloth.

The buttons may be sewn on, or stuck on if you are no needlewoman. Sewing takes longer, but it will be well worth the effort in the end!

AFTER A FURIOUS FIGHT—

THEY THINK I'M BOUND TO FAIL IN MY TASK. I'LL SHOW THE BOUNDERS!

NO ONE CAN HOLD A CANDLE TO ME FOR INITIATIVE.

HEY! I SMELL BURNING!

IT'S ONLY MY SHOES. SINCE THAT RUN ALONGSIDE TESS'S CAR THEY HAVEN'T STOPPED SMOKING!

A PEPPER POT WAS MY ONLY WEAPON.

AAAAH—

AAAAH—

AAAAH—

TAKING ADVANTAGE OF THE CONFUSION, I SCOOPED UP THE COINS.

HEY, WHO'S PINCHING THE LOOT?

TAKE THAT, YOU DIRTY DOUBLE—CROSSER.

I'LL BAG THE CROOKS WHEN I'VE BAGGED THE MONEY!

A CHORUS OF SNEEZES PLUNGED THE ROOM INTO DARKNESS.

I'LL SHOW 'EM MY SECURITY SERVICE IS NOT TO BE SNEEZED AT!

—CHOOOO!

I SOON DEALT WITH—OOPS!

WHACK!

WOW! TAKE CARE!

NOW LET'S SEE YOU SCOOP UP THESE COINS!

SOME SECURITY SERVICE! YOU WOULDN'T SECURE ANY CONTRACTS FROM US!

vacant possession

I LAY on my bed gazing at the ceiling, and reflected that life could be jolly unfair at times. At school, some girls grumbled about their brothers, but, believe me, sisters can be far worse. At least they were at our house.

I spent all my time running round after mine, just like a slave or something. And Mum shamelessly encouraged it, so that I didn't have a leg to stand on.

It was, "Oh, Cassie, make Belinda some coffee, will you?" Or, "Sew this button on for Belinda, Cassie," or, "Take the evening paper up to Belinda, dear."

"It makes me cross," I muttered, picking up the old teddy that still lives on my bed. "Just because she's nineteen and pretty and clever, she has it made."

Teddy stared back at me with his one good eye.

Of course, I'm not like Cinderella, but I do have to put up with Belinda's hand-me-downs (which are roughly five years out of date by the time they fit me), and my bedroom is a cross between a large cupboard and a kennel.

Honestly, I think that was what I envied Belinda most—her bedroom.

"You'd like to live up in Belinda's room, wouldn't you, Ted?" I said, prodding him. "It's much lighter and lots bigger."

Not only that, but it was right at the top of the house and sort of self-contained, as it had once been a bed-sit. It had a gas ring and loads of shelf space, which was all wasted on Belinda because she can't boil an egg and never has time for reading, whereas my books overflow into a box under my bed, and I adore cooking. It's the only thing I'm good at, really.

Mum's voice came floating up the stairs.

"Cassie, come and start getting tea, dear. Belinda wants to go out early."

I was halfway down the stairs before I realised it. But, as I was still feeling irritable and disgruntled I stamped into the kitchen and said, "Why should I?"

Well, Mum and Belinda turned round in such

hurt surprise that I hastily changed it to, "Oh, OK! What do you want? A boiled egg?"

'The trouble now,' I thought, as I watched the egg-timer, 'is that they've got so used to me jumping when they say jump, that they think I'm being awkward when I dig my toes in.

'Perhaps Belinda would leave home? That would solve two problems at once. No more slavery — and vacant possession of her bedroom. But no,' I told myself sadly, 'she's got a good job at the bank. There's no need for her to leave home, unless, unless . . .'

Why hadn't I thought of it before? She could get married, couldn't she? Gosh, she was old enough, and she'd been going round with that David Young for ages.

In fact, I quite liked him.

We all did. Not that I'd taken much notice of her romantic tangles in the past, but perhaps I should, from now on.

"I'll give them a bit of encouragement," I muttered, feeling quite excited at the idea.

"What did you say, Cassie dear?" asked Mum, looking up from ironing. "If you've finished Belinda's egg, could you just iron her skirt?"

Dutifully, I changed jobs, my mind busy with plans. What I had to do was persuade David Young to pop the question. Well, I'd read enough magazines to know the ropes. What was needed was a nice peaceful, romantic setting.

So when Belinda was getting ready to go out, I took her up a cup of coffee, and casually walked over to the window.

"It's a lovely night," I said, peering out.

"Oh, yes?"

Belinda was busy with her make-up.

"The moon is full," I remarked, "bathing everything in a soft light."

Belinda looked up at that all right, and gazed at me as if I was slightly round the twist.

'Gosh! I mustn't overdo it,' I thought.

"I mean it makes everything look sort of romantic," I explained. "Like a novel. I bet it's nice in the park by the river. What with all the stars and things," I added hastily, as she gulped down her coffee.

I followed her downstairs feeling that my ideas had fallen on stony ground, but when David arrived, I found that she had been listening after all.

"Let's go for a walk in the park," I heard her suggest as they went out.

Well, I was all agog to hear if anything happened, but Mum made me go to bed at half-past nine, so I must have been asleep when Belinda came in.

But as there was no excitement the next morning, I guessed that nothing had come of it.

ALL TOO EASY

BY now, I'd set my heart on Belinda's room. I'd even decided that I'd have a go at redecorating it in yellow and white, and I kept seeing myself in a dashing apron, rustling up tasty little snacks for my friends.

I might even ask Miss Todd, our Domestic Science teacher. She's ever so popular with our crowd.

But first, Belinda must go.

'Well,' I thought, 'perhaps David Young doesn't go for the romantic touch, after all. Maybe he needs something more cosy and intimate to encourage him.' So when Sunday came and I found that Belinda had a date with David in the afternoon, I had to do a quick think.

"David's bringing his Dad's car," I heard Belinda telling Mum in the kitchen.

"What a pity it's such a nasty day," Mum replied. "Not much fun going anywhere in this weather."

I glanced out of the window. The wind was blowing a gale and sending the rain beating against the glass. No, not very nice, I silently agreed.

But then I suddenly had an idea.

"Just the day for going to the sea," I said, breezing into the kitchen, where Mum and Belinda were doing the vegetables.

"Don't be silly, Cassie dear," Mum said. "Haven't you looked outside?"

"Yes," I said cheerfully. "But I always love the sea when it's rough, don't you? Sitting in a car watching the waves pounding on the beach, and listening to the rain beating on the windows makes you feel all cosy and safe."

I glanced over at Belinda who was certainly listening, and looking thoughtful.

"But, Cassie, dear," Mum protested, playing right into my hands, " there would be nothing to do except sit in the car, and everything would be deserted and shut."

"That's what I meant, Mum." I giggled at her puzzled face. "Some people like that sort of thing."

"It would be nice to have a bit of sea air," Belinda put in, with a faraway look in her eyes. And I knew that she'd got the point.

Well, I felt so confident that Belinda would come back safely engaged after a cosy heart-to-heart on the Prom, that I went up to her room while she was out and did a bit of measuring. After all, I'd definitely need new curtains, and I might even try my hand at papering one wall.

However, I was doomed to disappointment, because Belinda returned unengaged, and visions of imminent vacant possession faded rapidly again.

But I was not going to be outdone. I must just think of something else, I told myself. What I needed was a situation that would reveal Belinda as a very suitable wife. Glamorous, yet domesticated, I decided.

Now, what would fit the bill?

In a flash it came to me. Dinner for two, cooked by Belinda's own fair hands, and with Belinda playing the gracious hostess, all dolled up in that dress she'd got for her birthday party.

Naturally, it would have been my fair hands that would have actually produced the meal, but David needn't know that. He'd only see a glamorous and competent candidate for the Housewife-of-the-Year stakes.

If that didn't prod him in the right direction, nothing would.

It was all too easy really. One evening, I left a magazine open at a picture of a couple tenderly holding hands over a candle-lit supper table, and another day I found a cook book with a chapter entitled "The Way to a Man's Heart," and left this casually on Belinda's chair.

Now, she doesn't work in a bank for nothing. She can put two and two together O K.

By the time I muttered something about dinner parties at home, she took me up on it as if she'd thought of the idea herself.

"I was thinking I'd like to give David a meal one evening, Mum," she said. "When you and Dad are out, I mean."

Mum looked doubtful at first as well she might. She knew the extent of Belinda's cooking only too well, but then she looked at me.

"Well, of course, Cassie can give you a hand," she suggested in a relieved sort of way.

"Yes, O K," I said carelessly. "I don't mind if I do."

TWO FOR ONE

YOU would have thought we were entertaining Steve McQueen or somebody, the fuss Belinda made over choosing the menu, but eventually we agreed on something simple but tasty, and when the great evening came, I must say that Belinda did do her share of the preparations.

'Perhaps she's not so bad after all,' I thought, when at last we were ready and she'd gone up to change. And I peered with satisfaction through the hatch at the gleaming table. She certainly knew about the finishing touches, I thought. It all looked just right.

David must have thought so, too, because right from the start he looked happy and relaxed. In between dishing up the food and tidying around,

I listened shamelessly to their conversation through the hatch. It was boring really.

And I was just thinking I'd better make some coffee when I heard David say, "Darling Belinda," so I put my eye to the crack and saw that they were holding hands across the table.

'Now,' I thought, 'is he going to?'

He was.

"Belinda, darling," he repeated. "Would you like to cook me chicken casserole and lemon meringue pie every Saturday night for the rest of our lives?"

Well, fair's fair. I didn't wait to see what happened next. I'm not completely shameless.

So I rattled away with pots and pans, while making coffee, until Belinda appeared, looking dreamy and starry-eyed.

"Oh, Cassie," she said. "Guess what? David and I are going to be married in the autumn."

I tried to look suitably surprised, and had no trouble at all in looking pleased.

"That's marvellous," I told her. "Great news."

"There's only one little thing," she went on, as she picked up the coffee tray. "Of course we haven't got enough for a deposit on a house yet, so we thought we'd turn my room back into a proper bed-sit, and live there for a bit."

. . . . .

I put the coffee pot down carefully, so that I shouldn't feel inclined to throw it at her. I could hardly believe it. After all my scheming, not only was I not getting vacant possession, but I'd very likely landed myself with another slave-driver as well.

'Well,' I thought, as I began to giggle slightly hysterically, 'it just goes to show that you don't always get what you bargain for.'

Next time I'll think twice before I interfere in anything!

The End.

BIG 'N' BERTHA

As far as Bertha's Dad was concerned, the family dog, Big, was just a BIG nuisance!

WHAT A MESS! THIS IS THE LAST STRAW!

BERTHA!

GET THIS LOT CLEANED UP— NOW!

IT'S NICE TO SEE THAT HAIRY HEARTHRUG DOING SOME WORK FOR A CHANGE.

PERFECT! THEY DESERVE A REWARD FOR THIS.

Later—

LUCKY THE ICE-CREAM VAN WAS PASSING.

"BERTHA'S PAD KEE POUT!"

AAAAH! SO THIS IS WHERE YOU PUT ALL THE STUFF!

GET RID OF THIS JUNK, DO YOU HEAR? I WANT TO SEE THIS BEDROOM, AND THE GARDEN, ABSOLUTELY SPOTLESS!

A FIRM HAND IS ALL THAT'S NEEDED.

THEY REALLY HAVE DONE WELL. I'M QUITE PROUD OF THEM.

AS A SPECIAL TREAT, I'LL TAKE YOU FOR A RUN IN THE CAR.

C'MON, BIG! I THINK WE'D BETTER GO FOR A RUN ON FOOT, AS FAST AS WE CAN!

WHAT'S MY SIGN?

Astrologers say that, depending on when we were born, our personalities were influenced by one of the twelve constellations which make up the Zodiac. Over the page, there are twelve different sets of questions and each set relates to one of the Zodiac constellations. Answer the questions in each set with either yes, no or sometimes and when you have finished, see which set you have answered all, or mostly, yes's to. Now look at the alphabet letter which heads that set and read the corresponding type panel to discover the sort of personality you have reflected.

If you find that your personality matches the one that's supposedly typical of your own birth sign, then perhaps there's something in what Astrologers say after all! If, on the other hand, you discover your personality matches that of another birth sign, perhaps you didn't answer the questions truthfully!

Whether or not you believe in Astrology, it's fun!

A.

1—Do you like expensive clothes? `YES` Y
2—Do you tend not to have strong likes and dislikes? `YES` Y̶
3—Do you fancy yourself as a bit of an organiser? `YES` Y
4—Are you ambitious? `YES`
5—Do you bottle-up your feelings rather than express them? `NO` Y
6—Are you able to get over disappointments easily? `NO` Y
7—Do you think a sense of humour is important? `YES` Y
8—Do dark-haired boys appeal to you more than fair-haired ones? `YES` N
9—Do you dislike planning ahead? `NO` N
10—Do perfectionists irritate you? `YES` Y   7

B.

1—Do you love food? Y `YES`
2—Do you manage your money well? Y `YES`
3—Is your life usually well organised? Y `NO`
4—Does the idea of playing hostess at parties appeal to you? Y `NO`
5—Are you easily jealous? N `YES`
6—Do you long to be appreciated by everyone you meet? Y `YES`
7—Would you say that tact wasn't your strong point? N `YES`
8—Do you have a great need for security? N `NO`
9—Do you find you get on best with practical people? Y `YES`
10—Do sophisticated people appeal to you? Y `NO`   7

C.

1—Do you love interesting conversations? `YES` Y
2—Does a job involving helping people appeal to you? `YES` Y
3—Are you bored when you're not actively involved in something? `YES` Y
4—Are you naturally the life and soul of parties? `YES` Y
5—Do you believe in worrying about tomorrow when it comes? `NO` N
6—Does personal freedom mean a lot to you? `YES` Y
7—Would you say you were a girl of many moods? `YES` N
8—Do you like a constant change of friends? `YES`NO N
9—Do jealousy and possessiveness annoy you? `YES` Y
10—Do you often analyse yourself? `NO` N   Y

D.

1—Are you too sensitive for your own good? `Yes`
2—Do you believe that honesty is definitely the best policy? `NO`
3—Do you have a vivid imagination? `Yes`
4—Are you prone to 'deep' moods? `no`
5—Do you enjoy cooking and housework? `Yes`
6—Are you economical with your money? `Yes`
7—Are you easily displeased? `NO`
8—Are you a romantic? `Yes`
9—Do you tend to take life too seriously? `NO`
10—Are you happy with the security of routine? `Yes`

E.

1—Do you possess a fiery temper? `NO`
2—Are you generous? `Yes`
3—Do you enjoy a good argument? `NO`
4—Do you like being independent? `Yes`
5—Are you extravagant with your money? `NO`
6—Does flattery work with you? `NO`
7—Do you always think carefully before making moves? `Yes`
8—Does entertaining people appeal to you? `Yes`
9—Do you have fixed opinions about things? `Yes`
10—Have you an optimistic approach to life? `Yes`

F.

1—Are you a perfectionist? `NO`
2—Does insecurity frighten you? `NO`
3—Are you often over-critical? `Yes`
4—Are you a methodical, painstaking worker? `NO`
5—Are you a homely person? `Yes`
6—Does untidyness irritate you? `Yes`
7—Are you very rarely impulsive? `Yes`
8—Do you enjoy planning ahead? `Yes`
9—Are you shrewd with your money? `NO`
10—Do you often take things too personally? `Yes`

G.

1—Do you hate being idle? `Yes`
2—Are you an animal lover? `NO`
3—Do you believe in being tactful at all times? `NO`
4—Do you love beautiful things? `Yes`
5—Are you often indecisive? `Yes`
6—Do you dislike arguments? `NO`
7—Do you find you are a popular person? `Yes`
8—Does helping and advising people appeal to you? `Yes`
9—Do you find small children irritating? `NO`
10—Do you use flattery? `NO`   5

H.

1—Do you find it hard to forgive and forget? `NO`
2—Are you jealous and possessive? `NO`
3—Are you often intensely emotional? `NO`
4—Do you choose your friends carefully? `Yes`
5—Have you a critical approach to life? `Yes`
6—Do you have very fixed opinions and views? `Yes`
7—Are you only really happy when you're secure? `NO`
8—Does loyalty in a friendship mean a lot to you? `Yes`
9—Do you brood when discontented? `Yes`
10—Do weak-willed people annoy you? `Yes`

I.

1—Are you an optimist? `NO`
2—Do you believe in living life to the full? `YES`
3—Do you loathe jealousy and possessive-ness? `YES`
4—Is it hard for you to resist a challenge? `YES`
5—Are you keen on the outdoor life? `YES`
6—Do you act impulsively? `NO`
7—Are you keen to have lots of friends? `YES`
8—Are you happiest wearing casual clothes? `YES`
9—Do you read a lot? `YES`
10—Are you quite often lucky? *8* `YES`

J.

1—Are you sentimental? `YES`
2—Do camping and caravanning appeal to you? `YES`
3—Do you find it hard to hide your feelings? `NO`
4—Have you a keen sense of humour? `YES`
5—Do you have strong need to feel secure? `NO`
6—Do you find it easy to save money? `YES`
7—Are you shy with strangers? `NO`
8—When only mildly disappointed, do you feel despondent? `NO`
9—Are you a pessimist? `NO`
10—Do you find it hard to adapt to unfamiliar circumstances? *4* `NO`

K.

1—Do you prefer having a lot of friends to a 'best' one? `NO`
2—Does science fiction fascinate you? `NO`
3—Do you tend to analyse everyone you meet? `NO`
4—Do narrow-minded people irritate you? `YES`
5—Are you unconcerned by what people think of you? `NO`
6—Does it take a lot for you to feel emotional? `NO`
7—Are you always coming across things you want to change? `YES`
8—Do you enjoy argumentative discussions? `YES`
9—Would you say you were a bit of a rebel? `NO`
10—Does being independent mean a lot to you? *A* `YES`

L.

1—Are you indecisive? `NO`
2—Do you often feel you are treated unfairly? `NO`
3—Are you secretive? `NO`
4—Do you often act on instinct? `NO`
5—Are you easily hurt? `YES`
6—Do you often live in a world of your own? `NO`
7—Do you rarely feel completely content? `NO`
8—Have you a vivid imagination? `YES`
9—Do you often make 'mountains out of molehills'? `YES`
10—Do you have high standards and ideals? *4* `YES`

A

ARIES 21st MARCH—20th APRIL

You are a typical Arien—impulsive, optimistic, carefree, fun-loving and confident.

You live for the minute and worry about tomorrow when it comes—although worry is perhaps the wrong word, since you rarely feel anything is worth worrying about! 'Things will sort themselves out sooner or later'—that's your attitude to any problems you may be faced with. Emotionally, you belong to one of the most stable signs of the Zodiac—easily able to forget disappointments by involving yourself in new interests. Being true to your sign, your only faults are selfishness and impatience. You tend to show interest in your own affairs more readily than in those of your friends. This, however, may be partly due to your 'inability' to show great interest in other people. You are quite happy to feel within yourself that you like or admire someone, but don't see the need to show your feelings. Your impatience reflects itself in the way you continually start on some new hobby or project only to lose interest half-way through, resulting in your abandoning it completely! It takes something or someone very special before your interest is truly awakened and held for good.

B

TAURUS 21st APRIL—21st MAY

Being a typical Taurean, you are determined, reliable, careful and artistic.

You are the sort of person who knows exactly what she wants and how to get it. Your determination allows you to fight for things you want, and, no matter how many obstacles you encounter, you see things through to the bitter end! This determined streak is reflected in the fact that you have very fixed opinions and often aren't able to see other people's points of view. In friendships you are trustworthy and loyal and expect the same in return. Nevertheless, you are realistic about disappointments and never 'bury your head in the sand'. You have a strong need for security, so that anything you do is unlikely to be outrageous or out of the ordinary. There is a good chance that you are involved in music or in the arts, but, if not, you will certainly have a keen appreciation of one or the other. The main Taurean faults are obstinacy and possessiveness, both of which could land you in awkward situations. Try to be more open-minded about things and accept that, although your opinions may be valid, they are not the only ones worth listening to.

C

GEMINI 22nd MAY—21st JUNE

Quick-witted, lively, versatile, imaginative and 'always on the go'—that's the typical Gemini.

You believe in living life to the full. This is evident in the number of hobbies and active interests you have. There must be several 'irons in the fire' before you can feel content. You adore meeting people and probably have a large, ever-changing circle of friends. Emotion is something you very rarely feel, simply because you are far too busy to become emotionally involved with any one thing. Thus, you seldom feel unhappy or disappointed, and even when you do, it is short-lived. You are happiest when you are among people, loving stimulating conversation. This makes you a popular person and sure to make any party go with a swing. Being so restless, you find it easy to feel impatient. If you start on something and lose interest—which you often do—you merely abandon it gaily and move on to something else. Consequently, you could have the reputation of being a little unreliable at times. Learn to force yourself to finish something you start, instead of leaving a trail of half-completed jobs behind you. You should find the bit of effort that's needed very rewarding.

D

CANCER 22nd JUNE—22nd JULY

Being a true Cancerian, you are sensitive, emotional and patient.

You tend to react to your emotions rather than to your reason. Because your own feelings can be so easily hurt, you are naturally kind and sympathetic towards other people. Also, being so honest and reliable, you expect to see the same qualities in others, so that, if someone lets you down, you can't forget it easily. It's not because you hold a grudge, however, but because of the bitter disappointment that you feel and the time you spend trying to work out why it happened. Loyalty means a great deal to you; thus, you are likely to have one carefully-chosen close friend rather than several casual acquaintances. Because you take life seriously, it probably takes a lot to content you. 'The Big, Bad World' is more than just a cliché to you. You are happiest with your family and with those people you know and completely trust. You do not welcome changes in your routine, since these, you feel, could lead to insecurity—something you dread. Your main faults are a tendency to brood, and possessiveness. Often, when things go wrong, you worry about the matter so much, it becomes distorted out of all proportion. Your possessiveness shows in the way you often seize something, and then, like a crab, would rather lose a claw than let it go!

E

LEO 23rd JULY—23rd AUGUST

Proud, trusting, energetic and domineering—these are your most prominent characteristics, being a typical Leo.

You love to be admired and have attention paid to you. Consequently, leadership in anything appeals to you, for there you can be yourself in as many know you are appreciated. You also love to involve yourself in as many active interests as you can, and sport especially has great appeal for you. In friendships you never expect too much and don't waste your time asking from someone what is not in his or her power to give. Uncomplicated, fun-loving people appeal to you most; 'deep' and pessimistic types bore you. Being so warm-hearted and generous, you make a terrific friend, always good for a laugh and ready for any adventure. Pride is well-developed in you and acts as a protective shield, so that harsh words and actions do not easily hurt you. Your main fault is conceit. Sometimes your need for admiration can get so out of proportion; it becomes almost an obsession with you. Also, an insistence on always being 'top dog' could mean a refusal to be content with anything that's second-best.

F

VIRGO 24th AUGUST—23rd SEPTEMBER

Being a typical Virgo means you are industrious, methodical, discriminating and a perfectionist.

Every action is carefully thought out and carried out in great detail. You never take chances, since you think this to be foolish. Another of your characteristics is that you tend to be a little too critical of things. Consequently, it takes a lot to please you and little to displease you. But no matter how much something or someone annoys you, the source is rarely the target for your abuse. Instead, anger and resentment fume within you, making you too tongue-tied with rage to do anything about it! It usually takes a lot of time before you become involved in a close relationship with someone, but when you do, your loyalty is long-lasting. Your only fault—although it is more of a shortcoming—is that the natural reserve you display to people can sometimes make you appear standoffish. People may find it difficult to get much response from you, so that you may often suffer from spells of loneliness. Try to be more open—you're really a very nice person to get to know!

G

LIBRA 24th SEPTEMBER —23rd OCTOBER

Restless, artistic, talkative and intelligent—these are the foremost characteristics of a typical Libran.

You probably find yourself very popular because of your natural charm and genuine appreciation of what is good in others. You may even find people coming to you with their problems since you are understanding and have a keen sense of what is just and fair. Displays of temper and heated arguments distress you because you believe in treating disagreements in a civilized manner. Because you are so willing to please, this quality could lead to friends taking an unfair advantage of your kind nature. Your restlessness stems from the fact that you are an excitement-seeker, and since life for the majority of the time is pretty monotonous, it follows that you are going to feel restless much more often than you are going to feel content. This difficulty you have in coming to terms with 'real life' forms the basis of your artistic talent and love of all that is beautiful and artistic. Apart from the danger you run of becoming over-discontent with life, your other fault is indecisiveness. When faced with having to make your own decisions, you spend so much time 'sitting on the fence' and, 'seeing both sides' that it becomes almost impossible for you to take any positive action.

H

SCORPIO 24th OCTOBER—22nd NOVEMBER

Jealous, deep-feeling, independent and critical—these are the characteristics which make you a predominantly Scorpio person.

Although on the surface you appear shy and reserved, beneath this 'outer wrapping' lies a very strong personality—a fact which probably surprises many people when it reflects itself in sudden bursts of temper. When your sights are set on something you want, you'll do everything in your power to get it. However, you will always go about it fairly, since it is not in your nature to be ruthless. Your naturally critical nature results in you having keen likes and dislikes. You can argue explicitly as to why you like something or dislike another thing and nobody can influence you to the contrary, no matter how hard they try! Personal relationships are probably more than often troublesome since you can easily feel jealous and very possessive towards close friends. Try to be less demanding in friendships and accept people for what they are rather than criticize them for what they aren't. Although people admire your sense of independence and respect your high principles, be careful not go give the impression that only a few people are 'good' enough to deserve your friendship.

I

SAGITTARIUS 23rd NOVEMBER—21st DECEMBER

Candid, impatient, curious, impulsive and freedom-loving—that's you!

You are a very well-balanced sort of person with a light-hearted attitude to life. You love to feel free to please yourself, but patience is a quality you don't possess, so that you can feel agitated if things don't go your way. Impulsiveness is something you find hard to control and you can only plan ahead on rare occasions usually connected with matters of vital importance to you. You are probably a country-lover and enjoy sporty pastimes. This stems from your need for independence and freedom. Very close friends don't really appeal to you, since you much prefer to meet and make lots of casual friends. You will be popular with everyone you meet because people admire your honesty and optimism. Also, your thirst for knowledge makes you an interesting and intelligent person to know. Your only faults are that you tend to be a bit too impatient at times and that your casual outlook on life often extends to matters which should be approached more seriously. Be careful not to be careless!

J

CAPRICORN 22nd DECEMBER—20th JANUARY

Practical, reserved, responsible, persevering and cautious—these are the characteristics which make you a typical Capricorn.

You are a very steady, 'down-to-earth' sort of person and those who know you can trust and rely on you without fear of being let down. You can plan ahead responsibly and don't like making spur-of-the-moment decisions unless circumstances force it upon you. Although shy in the company of strangers, if you decide you like them, it doesn't take you long to come out of your shell. You are also a very hard worker and are probably successful at school. If not, you will continually try to better yourself until you are satisfied you have reached the full extent of your capabilities. This ambitious streak extends to out-of-school activities, too, so that any hobbies you have will be taken seriously. You are not always serious-minded, however, because you possess a marked sense of humour which will endear many people to you. Your friends mean a great deal to you—partly because you value a good, loyal friendship highly, and partly because you do not enjoy being on your own. However, with your sort of personality, there's not much chance of that!

K

AQUARIUS 21st JANUARY—19th FEBRUARY

Honest, kind, independent, broad-minded and probing—those characteristics are typical of the true Aquarian.

You are very popular—people born under this sign are probably about the most popular in the Zodiac. Your popularity is basically because you have a very honest and genuinely kind personality. Your feeling for all mankind is intense; so much so that you want, and have the ability, to understand almost everyone you meet. Friendships for you are based on this understanding and on personal esteem—and since you are the most sincere of people, your affections are well worth having. However, being so independent, you can easily survive without any close or long-lasting friendships. You are probably very interested in world affairs and have strong views on bettering or changing existing systems. Nevertheless, you are broad-minded and quite happy to change your views if you come to realise they are at fault. You love to, and have a great capacity to learn, so your common-sense and intelligence level is high. One of your faults is that you can, on occasions, be a bit of a rebel, brought about by a reluctance to become involved in something you believe to be completely wrong. Also, your honesty can lead you to be outspoken at times, but generally, you can keep both faults under control.

L

PISCES 20th FEBRUARY—20th MARCH

Indecisive, sensitive, gentle, dependent and moody—that's you.

Your symbol displays two fishes, attached at the tail but attempting to swim in opposite directions. This signifies your reaction when faced with a decision. You will move this way and that, achieving no positive result. It also means that you often hide your true feelings by displaying the opposite ones. You are so good at this that it takes someone who knows you really well to know how you are really feeling. However, even that person can be thrown by your sudden secretive moods. Quite often, and for no apparent reason, you become quiet and secretive, shutting out even your closest friends. These moods, however, don't last long and for most of the time you are kind and gentle and display a sort of dependence which most people find appealing. Because you are very easily hurt, your choice of friends depends on how understanding of your sensitive nature they are. You're probably satisfied to have one or two close friends and nothing more. The typical Piscean fault, apart from indecisiveness, is a tendency to read too much into simple situations. Because your emotions rule your life, disappointments and small upsets hit you unnecessarily hard, and happy events are dwelled upon with an unreal sense of elation.

PONY TALES

IF YOUR PONY IS LOST...

SOB! HOWL!

STOLEN...

SWAG

OR STRAYED...

HOW WOULD YOU DESCRIBE HIM?

?

HE'S CALLED BUSTER - HE'S FAT, AND HE BITES!

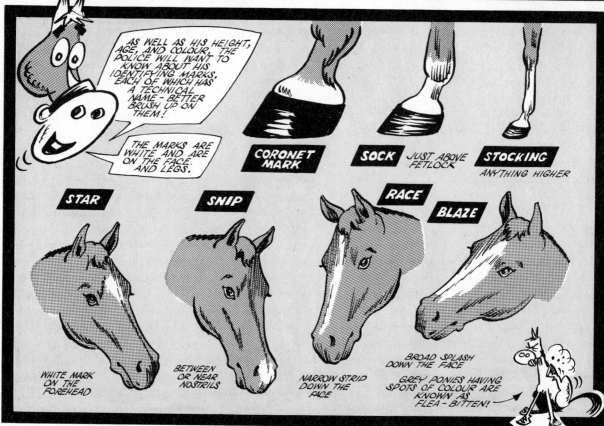

AS WELL AS HIS HEIGHT, AGE, AND COLOUR, THE POLICE WILL WANT TO KNOW ABOUT HIS IDENTIFYING MARKS, EACH OF WHICH HAS A TECHNICAL NAME - BETTER BRUSH UP ON THEM!

THE MARKS ARE WHITE AND ARE ON THE FACE AND LEGS.

CORONET MARK

SOCK JUST ABOVE FETLOCK

STOCKING ANYTHING HIGHER

STAR
WHITE MARK ON THE FOREHEAD

SNIP
BETWEEN OR NEAR NOSTRILS

RACE
NARROW STRIP DOWN THE FACE

BLAZE
BROAD SPLASH DOWN THE FACE

GREY PONIES HAVING SPOTS OF COLOUR ARE KNOWN AS FLEA-BITTEN!

HEY, COME ON, KIDS. BIG SMILES!

IT'S NO USE. THAT PAIR HAVE SPOILED IT FOR THEM. I WISH I COULD COME UP WITH A BRIGHT IDEA TO MAKE OUR KIDS FEEL SPECIAL.

On Friday afternoon—

HI, CHRIS! LISTEN, I'VE GOT AN EARLY CHRISTMAS PRESENT FROM AN AUNT. WANT TO SEE?

YES, PLEASE. I WISH SOMEBODY WOULD PRESENT ME WITH A BRIGHT IDEA FOR FIXING THOSE TWINS, THOUGH.

LOOK! A CINE CAMERA! GREAT, ISN'T IT?

ANDREW, I LOVE YOU!

WELL, THANKS! IT'S MUTUAL!

I LIKE YOUR AUNT, TOO! HOW DO YOU FANCY YOURSELF AS A FILM DIRECTOR, ANDREW?

AND PHOTOGRAPHER? I'M BEGINNING TO GET THE IDEA, CHRIS.

Next morning—

DON'T WATCH THE CAMERA, KIDS. PLAY AS THOUGH IT'S NOT THERE.

THEY'LL SOON GET USED TO IT, CHRIS.

And when the twins returned from the studio—

WE'VE BEEN MAKING FILMS, ALL THE MORNING. MOVING FILMS. ANDREW TOOK THEM.

THEY'LL BE SILLY OLD FILMS.

AND LOTS OF PEOPLE WON'T SEE THEM ON TELEVISION.

LOTS OF PEOPLE WILL SEE THEM. WE'RE GOING TO GIVE FILM SHOWS HERE AND AT THE COLLEGE.

SO THERE, SHOW-OFFS!

AND THE PEOPLE WILL LIKE US.

They did, too. At the first showing—

WE CAN SHOW OUR FILM AT THE HOSPITAL AND THE OLD FOLKS' HOME. WE CAN EVEN TAKE THE KIDS ALONG. THEY'LL ENJOY THAT.

THE TWINS ARE PEEVED— THEY'LL PROBABLY WANT TO LEAVE.

HUH! THEY'RE SO CONCEITED THEY'LL BE SURE THEY ARE STILL THE GREATEST.

Chris was right, and the twins still boasted, but—

OUR FILMS ARE MUCH, MUCH BETTER THAN THEIRS, JASON.

STILL AT IT, BUT NOW OUR KIDS JUST DON'T BOTHER ABOUT IT. AND IN THREE DAYS' TIME, THE TWINS GO HOME. I MUST REMEMBER TO SEND ANDREW'S AUNTIE A CHRISTMAS CARD, BLESS HER!

PONY TALES

SURPRISE — SURPRISE!

THE COMPLETED JIGSAW

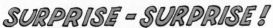

WELL, WHAT DO Y'KNOW?

IT'S ME!

LOT 309

OF COURSE, WE PONIES HAVE OUR REQUIREMENTS, TOO, AND WE ARE ALWAYS ON THE LOOK-OUT FOR THE PERFECT RIDER!

GIDDUP!

THIS KIND ARE STRICTLY FOR COMIC BOOKS, I'M GLAD TO SAY ...

... WHILE THIS TYPE IS FOUND ONLY IN MANUALS OF INSTRUCTION!

HERE'S ANOTHER JIGSAW — PUT IT TOGETHER AND YOU WILL FIND THE PERFECT RIDER!

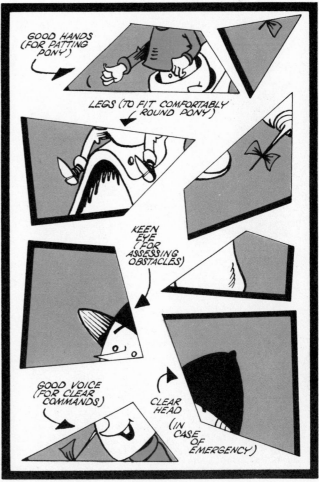

GOOD HANDS (FOR PATTING PONY)

LEGS (TO FIT COMFORTABLY ROUND PONY)

KEEN EYE (FOR ASSESSING OBSTACLES)

GOOD VOICE (FOR CLEAR COMMANDS)

CLEAR HEAD (IN CASE OF EMERGENCY)

WELL, FANCY THAT — IT'S ME!

THE RESULT!

BE A NUMBER ONE WIZARD!

a FIRST, COPY THE SIX CARDS SHOWN ONTO STIFF PAPER, THEN TELL A FRIEND TO THINK OF A NUMBER UP TO SIXTY.

b SPREAD THE CARDS OUT IN ANY ORDER AND ASK YOUR FRIEND TO POINT OUT WHICH ONES HER NUMBER APPEARS ON.

c JUST ADD UP THE NUMBERS IN THE TOP LEFT-HAND CORNERS TO FIND THE NUMBER THOUGHT OF.

TWELVE!

d FRIEND COLLAPSES IN ASTONISHMENT AND ADMIRATION.

TELL ANYBODY'S AGE - NUMBER OF THEIR HOUSE ETC!

The IRON-GREY COLT

THE grey colt moved uneasily. The sounds and smells of the loose-box were strange to him, and he was afraid. The doors were closed, shutting off the light. The colt stood in the deep straw, tensed to every sound that his quick ears could catch. When the top half of the door was opened, he sprang to the back of the box and stood trembling.

"Settled down, have you?" said a voice. "Have some fresh air."

The colt recognised the voice. He dimly remembered being caught from the freedom in which he had grown up, being loaded with other horses on to a noisy, rattling truck, and finally herded into the stable, where the doors had been shut on his frantic efforts to escape.

That voice had been present all the time, shouting at him when he was loose, and talking roughly about him when he had been captured.

"We can start on the two-year-old right away. He'll make a nice show hack next year. He hasn't been handled at all, though, so get a headcollar on him and we'll start teaching him to lead."

The colt looked at the faces peering at him over the door of his box. The hard-lined face of the man whose voice he knew, and the plain, round face of the girl with him.

When the faces went away the colt snorted his relief into the deep straw bedding, and examined the walls and floor of his box with his delicate nostrils.

His ears pricked forward, his eyes stared at nothing, as he picked up the smells of fresh straw and hay, other horses, and the strange smell of humans.

His head shot up as he heard footsteps approaching once more. This time the door opened, and the man and the girl came in, closing the door behind them.

"Hello, Star," the girl said. "Be a good boy, now, and let us get the headcollar on."

The colt stiffened at the voice. Every muscle in his sleek, dark body tensed. The two people were slowly drawing nearer to him as he stood trembling in the corner.

Suddenly he leapt forward past them, but the man leapt with him, and took a firm grip on the colt's nose with one hand, and grabbed his mane with the other.

Star snorted and jerked his head up, but the grip was still there, and, with lightning quickness, the girl was strapping the leather headcollar behind his ears.

Then the man and the girl left the box.

Star stood, head lowered, with all his senses concentrating on the object on his head. He waited for something to happen; when nothing did, he raised his head.

The headcollar jangled slightly, and swung against his nose. He froze, and waited again. He soon got used to the feel of the leather, but he did not forget his fright.

Star learned quickly. He learned that when he was tied up, the rope and headcollar held him fast and he could not get away. He learned that when the rope was in the hands of the trainer he could not get away either, nor must he hang back for fear of the stick tapping on his hindquarters.

He learned to trot in circles on the end of the long lunging rein, but all the time he watched the trainer standing there with his long whip. Star was always alert to his trainer's wishes, because he was frightened. He was never given confidence, never assured that he was doing well. If he misbehaved, he was punished, but if he did well the girl simply slapped him on the shoulder and led him back to his box.

He was introduced to the saddle and bridle in the same way he had been introduced to the headcollar. The cold saddle was thrown on his back, and the girths pinched up tight; the bit was forced between his teeth and the bridle strapped on.

Then he was left alone to find out that the tack would not harm him, and that the discomfort was not too great.

Finally, the day came when he was pronounced fit and ready to be ridden. The man with the rough voice and the girl trainer came into his stable where he was standing ready, saddled and bridled. As always, Star tensed himself, his large eyes never leaving the two people.

He flinched when the man took hold of his bridle, but stood quietly enough as the girl pulled down the stirrups and leaned her weight on his back. When she swung herself into the saddle, he humped his back, and his muscles bunched together in readiness. The man still gripped the reins, holding Star's head up, so the colt did nothing, but stood trembling under the unaccustomed weight.

"He seems quiet enough," the man said. "Shall I lead him about?"

The girl on Star's back nodded, so the man began to lead Star forward. At first Star wouldn't move, but he was pulled by the bit until he took a few steps. He was led out of the stable and through the yard towards the paddock where all his schooling had taken place.

DASH TO DISASTER

SUDDENLY Star rebelled. The heavy weight on his back frightened him, and the grip on his bridle irritated him. He could see freedom on the other side of the paddock fence. He threw his head into the air, loosening the man's hold on the reins, and then reared up, striking out with his forelegs until the man let go.

Star galloped across the paddock with the girl still on his back. Her frantic pull on the reins made no impression on his unschooled mouth, he merely pulled against it and ran harder. The fence was ahead of him and he knew he could jump it; he gathered himself for the take-off. As he rose into the air it became obvious that he had not allowed for the weight on his back unbalancing him.

There was a sickening crash as he plunged through the top rail.

The girl was thrown clear, but Star fell to the ground with the broken rail. He got to his feet and stood still among the debris of the fence. His head was hanging; the shock had knocked all rebellion out of him. Across his chest was an angry, open gash.

The girl was unhurt, and caught hold of Star's dangling reins.

"What got into him?"

The man with the rough voice was there, too.

"He's always been so quiet," he added angrily.

They led Star back to his stable. When the girl took off his saddle he swung his hindquarters towards her, and she had to dodge out of the stable.

The man tried to look at Star's wound, but the colt laid his ears flat back on his neck and struck out with his forelegs.

"We'll have to get the vet to stitch that wound," the man said. "I don't know how he's going to manage it. The horse has turned vicious."

Star stood listlessly in the safe corner of his box, nodding his head against his chest to keep the flies off his wound. When the vet came, it took five people to pin Star against the wall while the vet looked at the wound.

Mixed with his feelings of terror, Star felt anger, and he fought for all he was worth. A hitch of rope was taken around Star's top lip as a twitch, to distract his mind from the wound, and the vet worked quickly and painlessly.

Afterwards the two faces looked over the top of his door at him.

"We'll have to sell him now," said the man with the rough voice.

"He won't be any good for showing if he's blemished," the girl agreed.

"He may have to be put down if he's going to be vicious," the man went on.

When Star's wound had healed he was loaded into the noisy, dark horsebox and taken away. It was a long journey, and he grew tired with bracing his legs against the jolting and swaying of the horsebox.

He was finally unloaded and left in another loose-box.

He made a quick inspection of the straw and hay net, but he felt disinterested and did not bother to look over the door of his box to see if there were other horses. He stood in the corner, resting a leg, his ears turned back, not flicking forward to catch the sounds around him.

When someone came to look over his stable door, Star turned his hindquarters and continued to stand at the back of the box.

"Hello, my beauty." The voice was gentle, soothing. "Are you going to come over here? I've got something for you."

FRIENDLY PERSUASION

STAR'S curiosity overcame him, and he turned his head to look at the owner of the voice. His attention was immediately caught by a large, green bunch of grass that was being held out to him.

The voice continued, talking quietly to him and calling softly to him. He stared at the grass, ears forward, motionless. The voice floated about his ears; the grass waved tantalisingly in front of his eyes.

The colt took a few steps forward, and reached out his head as far as he could towards the grass. He stretched his neck, turning his head slightly, but his lips snapped on empty air.

He took another step, and this time managed to grasp a delicious mouthful. He chewed, staring thoughtfully at the rest of the grass, which now seemed a little farther away.

"Come on," said the girl who was holding out the grass. "Come a little nearer and you can have some more."

Star came a little nearer. He came forward until he was leaning over the stable door, tearing great mouthfuls of grass from the girl's hands.

"Good boy, Star," she said.

Very slowly she raised her hand to touch Star's neck. He pulled back at the touch, but there was still some grass, and soon he was letting the girl pat his neck, though he watched her warily while he ate.

When she opened the door to his box and came in, he shot back into the corner, making angry faces and threatening her with his hindquarters. She did not come after him, but stood by the door, talking to him.

"I'm not going to come to you," she said gently. "You must learn to come to me. I haven't any grass left, but if you come here you can have some hay."

She stood by the hay net, pulling pieces out and offering them to him. Once more he stood motionless, watching her every move, until, finally, his curiosity forced him to step forward and snatch wisps of hay out of her hands.

Gradually Star began to trust his new mistress. Every day she came to his box and called him over, and, as he grew friendlier, she patted him, and finally tied him up and brushed him. She talked to him all the time, running her hands soothingly down his neck.

Star began to look forward to her visits, and not only because of the hay she brought him. One day, his nostrils fluttered as she walked towards him, and he greeted her with a low whicker.

"Hello, Star!" said the girl, amused and pleased by this show of affection.

Star learned to be led all over again, this time walking beside his mistress with a confident, swinging stride, ears pricked and eyes taking in his surroundings with a lively interest. He was lunged in the field, and always there was a voice following him, praising him and encouraging him.

At the end of the lesson he came up to his mistress and took the grass she offered him, tickling her hand with his silky whiskers, and arching his neck under the rewarding pats.

When he was tacked up, the saddle was slid gently on to his back, and the girl always waited a few minutes for it to warm up before carefully doing up the girths; never too tight. She coated his bit with treacle, and let him take it himself rather than forcing it between his teeth.

One day the girl came to Star, and she was wearing a hard hat on her head. She brushed him and tacked him up, then slipped the headcollar over his bridle and tied him in the stable. Then she fussed around him, pulling down the stirrups and checking the girth.

"Last time this happened to you," she told him, "you were frightened. Don't be frightened now."

She leaned on the saddle, patting his neck, and then put one foot in the stirrup. Star stood still, so she quietly mounted, lowering herself slowly and carefully into the saddle.

Star remembered. His head shot up and his muscles tensed. He heard the familiar, soothing voice and felt the calming hand stroking his neck. Gradually he relaxed, and, after a few minutes, the girl got off.

"That wasn't too bad, was it?" she asked, patting his neck and gently pulling his ears.

She got on him every day after that, and let him walk round the loose-box to get used to her weight. Then she tied him in the stable yard and mounted him there. One day she didn't tie him, but got on him while he stood loose in the yard.

"Walk on, Star," she said.

Star knew the words from his lunging lessons, and he moved forward, uncertainly at first, but then faster. The reins gently guided him into the field.

Suddenly Star saw the rails ahead of him. The weight on his back, the grass under his feet, the freedom on the other side of the rails were all the same as before. Star remembered pain and fear, and he panicked. He jumped forward, pulling on the reins.

There was no answering pull, nothing to fight against.

"Steady, Star," the soft, gentle voice was in his ears. "We're only walking today. There's no need to leap about."

Star flicked one ear back, then forward again, staring at the rails and the freedom. He stood still, and the hand was on his neck, stroking him.

"What's wrong?" the voice soothed him. "Don't be frightened. I won't hurt you."

Star stared ahead of him, but his ears turned back to catch the voice. He trusted that voice.

"Walk on, Star."

Star turned away from the rails and walked confidently and calmly forward.

The End.

LAZY DAISY

In the next class, Daisy was hoping to relax.

THIS IS WILLOW BROOK, THE FAMOUS FASHION MODEL. SHE'S GOING TO GIVE YOU GIRLS MODELLING LESSONS AFTER SCHOOL.

OH, SUPER!

AFTER SCHOOL? HOW EXHAUSTING!

Later, the modelling class got under way.

I'LL CORRECT THE FAULTS, GIRLS.

YOU'RE JUST NOT LIVELY ENOUGH.

I'M UTTERLY EXHAUSTED!

PERHAPS YOU COULD MODEL HATS BETTER THAN CLOTHES. SEE WHAT YOU CAN DO WITH THESE.

OOF! ALL RIGHT, I'LL TRY.

NO, NO, NO! YOU SHOULD WALK UP AND DOWN WEARING EACH ONE! YOU'RE TOO LAZY TO GET A MODELLING JOB!

Later that week—

GIRLS, SOME OF YOU HAVE DONE VERY WELL AND HAVE ALREADY GOT PART-TIME MODELLING JOBS.

YES, I'M ONE OF THEM. I APPEAR IN STOB'S STORES ON SATURDAY.

On Saturday, Willow just had to see for herself.

HA-HA!

HO-HO!

I WONDER WHAT'S CAUSING THE LAUGHTER.

OH, NO! SHE CAN'T MODEL CLOTHES OR HATS, SO SHE MODELS A DAY-BED!

LEISURE GEAR

VAL OF THE VALLEY

VAL MARTIN, district nurse, was based in the village of Storrhurst in Storr Valley. One spring morning she was out on her rounds.

MAM! MAM, DON'T LEAVE ME! COME BACK, MAM!

WHAT'S THE MATTER WITH SUSAN LAWSON AND HER MOTHER?

PLEASE, MAM!

IT'S FOR YOUR OWN GOOD, SUSAN.

WHAT'S THE TROUBLE, MRS CARTER? CAN I HELP?

Mrs Carter explained that Susan was afraid of being left alone with her baby daughter.

I'VE BEEN SPENDING EVERY DAY WITH SUSAN UNTIL HER HUSBAND GETS HOME FROM WORK. THIS MORNING I DECIDED I JUST HAD TO BE FIRM WITH HER.

I SEE. WELL, YOUNG MUMS ARE OFTEN NERVOUS WITH THEIR FIRST BABY. SHE'LL GET OVER IT.

I WON'T! I KNOW I WON'T! OH, MAM!

YOU WOULDN'T DROP YOUR BABY, SUSAN, OR HURT HER. I'M SURE YOU WOULDN'T!

I'M NOT SO SURE, NURSE. SHE'S SO TINY AND LOVELY—AND IT WOULD BREAK MY HEART IF I WERE TO HURT OR FRIGHTEN HER.

Later—

POOR SUSAN IS REALLY SCARED. BUT SHE DOES LOVE HER BABY, AND MAYBE SOON THE LONGING TO HOLD LINDA WILL OVERCOME HER FEARS.

A week later—

SUSAN STILL WON'T LOOK AFTER THE BABY ON HER OWN, NURSE. LINDA'S GOING TO THINK I'M HER MOTHER IF THIS GOES ON MUCH LONGER. AND I'M WORRIED ABOUT SUSAN—SHE'S SO UNHAPPY.

I'LL TAKE SUSAN AND LINDA ON MY ROUNDS WITH ME THIS AFTERNOON. IT'S A LOVELY DAY, AND IT'LL MAKE AN OUTING FOR SUSAN.

EVERYONE'S SURE TO MAKE A FUSS OF THE BABY, AND THAT WILL MAKE SUSAN FEEL PROUD. IT MIGHT INCREASE HER CONFIDENCE.

That afternoon—

PINEWOOD FARM IS MY LAST CALL FOR THIS AFTERNOON—LAST HOPE, TOO, FOR NOW. LINDA'S HAD A LOAD OF COMPLIMENTS AND THAT'S PLEASED SUSAN, BUT I DON'T THINK IT'S BOOSTED HER CONFIDENCE.

GIVE ME A HAND WITH THE CARRY-COT, SUSAN.

I-I CAN'T, NURSE VAL. I-I'D BE SURE TO TRIP OVER MY FEET, AND TIP LINDA OUT!

Gran Tyler was the patient at Pinewood Farm, where she lived with her son and daughter-in-law.

HERE'S NURSE VAL, GRAN, AND SHE'S BROUGHT SUSAN LAWSON ALONG. SUSAN'S BABY IS BEAUTIFUL!

LET'S HAVE A LOOK, THEN. I LOVE BABIES. WHEN YOU'VE DRESSED MY LEG, NURSE, PERHAPS I COULD HOLD HER FOR A WHILE, EH?

After Gran's treatment, Val left her alone with Susan and the baby. A little later—

TAKE HER, SUSAN LASS, QUICKLY! MY OLD HANDS ARE GETTING VERY SORE— IT'S THE ARTHRITIS. HURRY!

OH, NO!

NURSE! NURSE VAL! COME QUICKLY!

WELL, I PLAYED MY PART, JUST LIKE NURSE VAL WHISPERED TO ME TO DO, BUT IT'S NOT GOING TO WORK.

Val, who was hiding just outside the door, waited for a couple of minutes, then—

OH! OH, THANK GOODNESS!

HER YELLS FOR HELP WERE SO PATHETIC, I JUST HAD TO GIVE IN.

An hour later—

HERE WE ARE, HOME AGAIN— WHAT ON EARTH ARE YOU DOING DOWN THERE?

HIDING! I JUST SPOTTED BRENDA WATKINS COMING THIS WAY, AND I DON'T WANT TO TALK TO HER. DON'T LET HER SEE ME, NURSE VAL, PLEASE!

HELLO, BRENDA. MARTIN LOOKS WELL.

HE ALWAYS DOES, NURSE. I'M AN EFFICIENT MUM. I'VE BEEN INTO RISEHOLME TO BUY SOME DRESS MATERIAL. I MAKE ALL MY OWN CLOTHES—I'VE A FLAIR FOR DRESSMAKING!

When Brenda had gone—

I'VE NEVER BEEN ABLE TO STAND BRENDA! SHE'S A CONCEITED CAT, AND BOSSY WITH IT!

SHE CERTAINLY IS A BIT MUCH.

When Mrs Carter arrived at the Lawsons' cottage the next morning, she told Susan she was going to the spring sales in Riseholme.

CAN'T I COME WITH YOU, MAM? IF YOU BATHED LINDA QUICKLY AND—

NO, DEAR. THERE'LL BE A CRUSH IN THE SHOPS AND IT'S BEST YOU AND THE BABY STAY HERE. I'VE ARRANGED A HELPER FOR YOU—I CAN HEAR HER COMING NOW. 'BYE!

OH, NO!

HI, SUSAN! CLUMSY AS EVER, I SEE!

YOUR MUM COULDN'T GET ANYONE ELSE TO STAY WITH YOU TODAY. SHE KNEW I COULD COPE. THOUGH WHY YOU SHOULD BE SCARED OF A LITTLE BABY BEATS ME. DAFT, I CALL IT.

SPITEFUL CAT! AND I'M STUCK WITH HER, UNLESS I GRAB THE PRAM AND RUN FOR IT.

RIGHT, I'LL GET HER BATHED AND DRESSED NOW. YOU WATCH ME, AND YOU'LL LEARN A LOT.

I'LL HAVE TO GO OUT BEFORE I STRANGLE HER! OH, BUT I CAN'T LEAVE MY LITTLE LINDA WITH HER. I'LL HAVE TO PUT UP WITH IT TILL MAM COMES BACK.

When Linda was dressed—

DON'T DO THAT, BRENDA! YOU MIGHT DROP HER.

DROP HER? NOT ME! OH, LOOK, SHE'S GOING TO CRY. MARTIN LOVES ME TO SWING HIM UP. STILL, HE'S STURDY. YOUR LINDA'S A BIT ON THE PUNY SIDE.

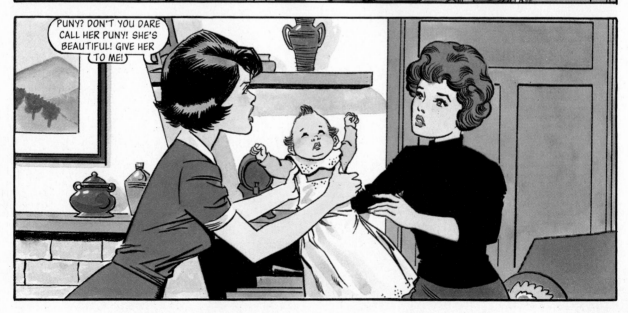

PUNY? DON'T YOU DARE CALL HER PUNY! SHE'S BEAUTIFUL! GIVE HER TO ME!

Val and Mrs Carter had planned things together.

A week later, Val was invited to a special ceremony.

After the ceremony—

NAIL KNOW-HOW!

nAIL and thread pictures are fascinating to make. Here's how to make a super "Birds in Flight" picture which will make a great gift or will look really stunning on your bedroom wall.

YOU WILL NEED—
A piece of plywood, 26 in. wide x 12 in. deep and ¼ in. thick. Black felt, 28 in. wide x 14 in. deep. 143 panel pins. A ball of Twilley's Goldfingering. A piece of backing felt, slightly smaller than the board. 1 in. squared graph paper (27 in. wide x 13 in. deep). A circle of orange felt, about 4 in. in diameter. Clear glue. Hammer.

TO MAKE UP THE DESIGN—
From the diagram below, make an actual size plan (26 in. x 12 in. deep) on your graph paper, using a dot to represent each nail. Mark each row of dots A1—A16, B1—B16, C1—C16, D1—D16, E1—E16, F1—F 16, G1—G16, H1—H16, and J1—J16. Join up the dots with a ruled line to get an accurate idea of the finished pattern.

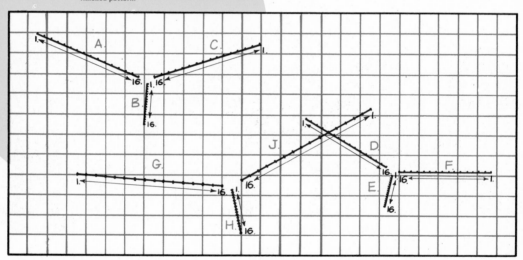

TO COVER THE BOARD—
Lay your black felt flat, removing the creases, then place the board in the centre. Spread some glue liberally over the side edges of the felt, then bring them over the wood, pulling the felt as taut as possible. Mitre the corners as shown, then glue the top and bottom edges firmly in place.

To give a neat finish to the back, glue the backing piece over the felt edges.

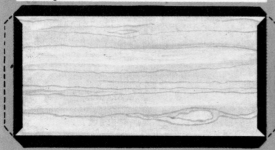

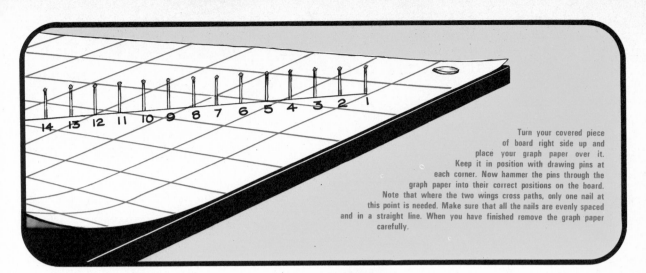

Turn your covered piece of board right side up and place your graph paper over it. Keep it in position with drawing pins at each corner. Now hammer the pins through the graph paper into their correct positions on the board. Note that where the two wings cross paths, only one nail at this point is needed. Make sure that all the nails are evenly spaced and in a straight line. When you have finished remove the graph paper carefully.

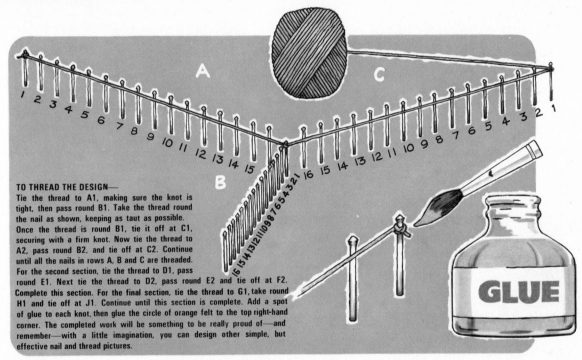

TO THREAD THE DESIGN—

Tie the thread to A1, making sure the knot is tight, then pass round B1. Take the thread round the nail as shown, keeping as taut as possible. Once the thread is round B1, tie it off at C1, securing with a firm knot. Now tie the thread to A2, pass round B2, and tie off at C2. Continue until all the nails in rows A, B and C are threaded. For the second section, tie the thread to D1, pass round E1. Next tie the thread to D2, pass round E2 and tie off at F2. Complete this section. For the final section, tie the thread to G1, take round H1 and tie off at J1. Continue until this section is complete. Add a spot of glue to each knot, then glue the circle of orange felt to the top right-hand corner. The completed work will be something to be really proud of—and remember—with a little imagination, you can design other simple, but effective nail and thread pictures.

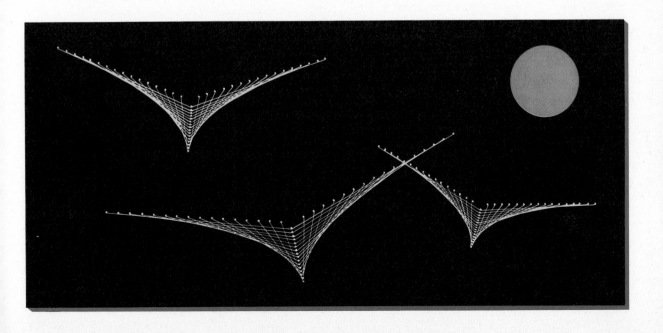

PICTURES THAT TELL A STORY ABOUT —
YOU!

We often don't know why we like something—we just do. Psychologists, however, claim that the simplest of personal tastes can give insight to people's characters.

Below are six pictures, each containing the same objects. These objects represent different aspects of your personality. The snake, for example, represents the ego. Look at the pictures and decide which one most appeals to you, then see the conclusions below to discover what your choice reflects about your personality.

You are a shy, retiring sort of person and need to feel very secure before you can come out of your shell and be happy. You probably feel most content with your family, relatives and close friends, so a hectic social life doesn't really appeal to you. You are also prone to pessimistic moods, but these are generally short-lived.

You have a well-balanced personality and your optimistic, carefree outlook makes you popular with everyone you meet. Thus, you probably have a large circle of friends, who, like you, love a gay social life. Although very attached to your family, you enjoy, and are trusted with, a fair amount of independence.

The most important person in your life is YOU! You tend to be a bit selfish in that you think of yourself before anyone else. You like to impress and people are usually impressed by your self-confidence and leadership qualities. However, you are very independent and can survive quite easily without a great deal of help from your family and friends.

You are an extrovert with a love of people and adventure. Your family probably play a backstage role in your life, whereas your friends mean so much to you, you tend to cling to them because of the security they offer. You hate being on your own, but it is easy for you to make friends, so it's unlikely that you will ever be lonely.

You are a loner and people may find it hard to understand you because you appear so detached. You are a deep-thinker but keep your thoughts to yourself. However, this and your fertile imagination probably finds an outlet through art or creative writing, at which you show great talent.

You are a bit of a "dark-horse"—shy on the surface, but deep-feeling underneath. You are probably a little wary of people and tend to think the worst of them rather than the best. You are a home-lover and choose your friends carefully because you can be easily hurt by people's thoughtless actions.

RAINBOW'S END

IT was a funny sort of day. Sunshine one minute, and showery the next. So, for part of the time you were flinging off your anorak feeling all cheerful, and the next moment huddling for shelter, trying not to be depressed.

That's what we were doing when we first saw the rainbow. Ann and me, I mean. We'd been taking our dogs for a run when it suddenly poured down, and we had to race for shelter under the chestnut tree on the green.

I was telling Ann about Mum not being able to get me another piano.

"Honestly, our old one is just about falling to bits. Even the piano tuner says it's nothing but a paradise for mice."

"Well, you can play at school," said Ann unfeelingly.

Of course, she doesn't know a middle C from an F sharp.

"Yes, but I need somewhere to practise in between. I can't get on if I don't practise," I grumbled.

And I really wanted to get somewhere with my music. It was about the only decent subject at school. What made me so mad was that Mum had been saving up to get a new second-hand one, if you see what I mean.

Then along comes my big sister, Kate, with plans for getting married at the end of the summer, so Mum has to start saving up for that instead.

Life can be so unfair.

"Life can be so unfair." I liked the phrase, and repeated it out loud for Ann's benefit.

But Ann wasn't listening. She was pointing to this super rainbow, much brighter than any I'd seen before. We could see almost the whole bright arc.

"Let's make a wish," said Ann, who's really very childish sometimes. "It might be magic, like a four-leaf clover."

"Silly," I replied. Then, seeing her face fall, I said, "Oh, all right, then."

It doesn't do any harm to humour her, I suppose. It wasn't very hard to guess what I wished, and, as Ann had been wanting a trouser suit for ages, I knew what her wish was, too.

But I hate standing still for long.

"Come on," I said. "Let's see if we can reach the end of the rainbow before it disappears. Look, it seems to come down at the edge of the wood."

Together we raced down the road, over the stile and into the fields. But long before we got to the woods, the rainbow had faded.

"Never mind, we might still find the crock of gold, or whatever it's supposed to be," I giggled. "Let's keep going."

"There's nothing here," gasped Ann breathlessly, a few minutes later. "Just grass."

"Well, you have to use your imagination," I told her. "It might be something symbolic."

Ann opened her mouth and shut it again. She didn't know what symbolic meant. For that matter, neither did I, but it sounded O K.

But I was just as amazed as Ann when, only seconds later, I actually spotted something.

"Look over here!" I yelled. "I *have* found something!"

VALUABLE FIND

WE gazed at it together as I held it in my hand. Not a crock of gold, certainly, but a beautiful antique-looking brooch, with what I call sort of wrought iron work round a lovely green emerald. Of course, it didn't look lovely till we'd wiped it with our hankies.

"Someone must have dropped it," breathed Ann.

"Well, that's obvious," I retorted. "It didn't really slide off the end of the rainbow. Come on, we'd better take it to the police station on the way home."

When we got there, Sergeant Roberts was delighted.

"It's already been reported as lost," he told us. "It belongs to Mrs Henderson-Smythe at the manor."

He gave it a polish with his hankie, which was somewhat cleaner than ours had been.

"It's valuable, you know," he remarked. "And it's got sentimental value, too. I'll telephone the lady and let you know what happens."

Well, so much happened in the next week that I practically forgot all about it. For one thing, Carol, my other sister, got herself engaged.

I was livid! Well, it put my piano even further down the list of priorities, didn't it?

Then I couldn't get the hang of some new maths, and that meant plugging away at it every evening with Mum breathing down my neck.

Ann's lucky — she's good at maths.

She also had luck in another way that week.

"Guess what!" she said one morning, sitting down beside me on the bus. "I've got that trouser suit after all."

"You lucky thing," I said. "That's super!"

"It must have been that rainbow wish that did the trick," she giggled.

"More like your Mum won at bingo," I said sarcastically. "But, anyway, I'm glad."

Then on Saturday luck came my way, too. Sergeant Roberts called at my house in the morning to say that Mrs Henderson-Smythe would like to thank me in person for returning her brooch.

"A summons from on high," I giggled.

Then, catching sight of Mum's face, I added, "I'll go over there this afternoon."

I told Ann, but she wouldn't come with me. She said that it was me who found the brooch, so I should get the thanks. Decent of her, really.

I'd never been to the manor before . . . well, only to fetes in the grounds, not to actually call at the house. It was all very grand. On each side of the steps up to the front door was a sort of giant stone acorn.

For a minute I went into a daydream, imagining giant stone squirrels coming to eat them. Then the door opened and a tall, slim lady looked out.

"I saw you coming up the drive," she smiled. "Come in, my dear."

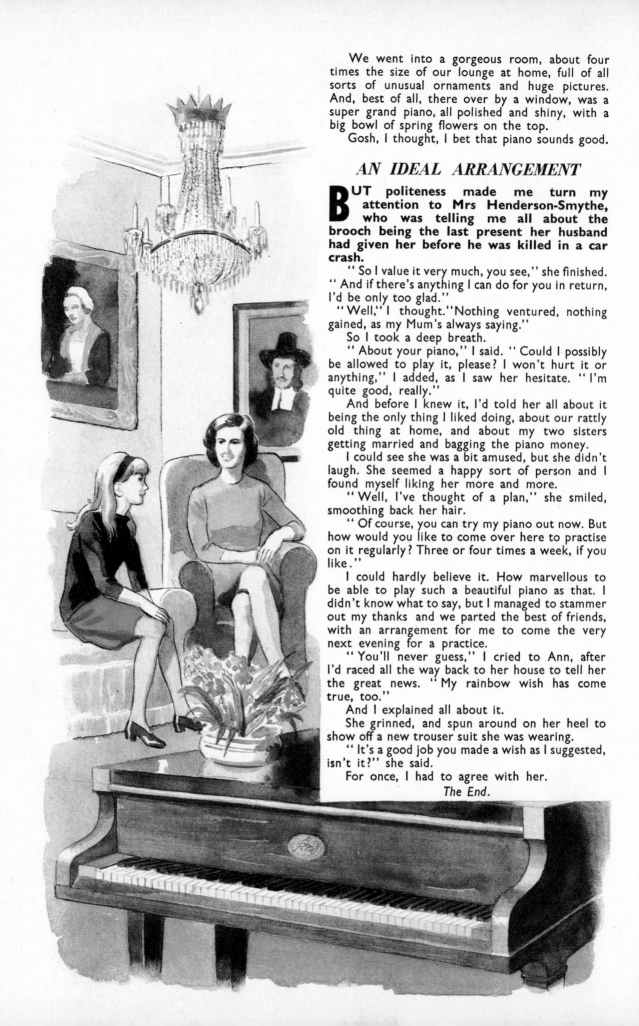

We went into a gorgeous room, about four times the size of our lounge at home, full of all sorts of unusual ornaments and huge pictures. And, best of all, there over by a window, was a super grand piano, all polished and shiny, with a big bowl of spring flowers on the top.

Gosh, I thought, I bet that piano sounds good.

AN IDEAL ARRANGEMENT

BUT politeness made me turn my attention to Mrs Henderson-Smythe, who was telling me all about the brooch being the last present her husband had given her before he was killed in a car crash.

"So I value it very much, you see," she finished. "And if there's anything I can do for you in return, I'd be only too glad."

"Well," I thought. "Nothing ventured, nothing gained, as my Mum's always saying."

So I took a deep breath.

"About your piano," I said. "Could I possibly be allowed to play it, please? I won't hurt it or anything," I added, as I saw her hesitate. "I'm quite good, really."

And before I knew it, I'd told her all about it being the only thing I liked doing, about our rattly old thing at home, and about my two sisters getting married and bagging the piano money.

I could see she was a bit amused, but she didn't laugh. She seemed a happy sort of person and I found myself liking her more and more.

"Well, I've thought of a plan," she smiled, smoothing back her hair.

"Of course, you can try my piano out now. But how would you like to come over here to practise on it regularly? Three or four times a week, if you like."

I could hardly believe it. How marvellous to be able to play such a beautiful piano as that. I didn't know what to say, but I managed to stammer out my thanks and we parted the best of friends, with an arrangement for me to come the very next evening for a practice.

"You'll never guess," I cried to Ann, after I'd raced all the way back to her house to tell her the great news. "My rainbow wish has come true, too."

And I explained all about it.

She grinned, and spun around on her heel to show off a new trouser suit she was wearing.

"It's a good job you made a wish as I suggested, isn't it?" she said.

For once, I had to agree with her.

The End.

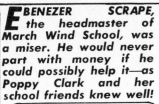

SKINFLINT SCHOOL

EBENEZER SCRAPE, the headmaster of March Wind School, was a miser. He would never part with money if he could possibly help it—as Poppy Clark and her school friends knew well!

WHAT A BREAKFAST! I'M STARVING! I'D GO OUT AND BUY A MEAL IF I HAD ANY MONEY! POPPY'S GOING TO ASK SCRAPE FOR SOME OF OUR OVERDUE POCKET-MONEY!

WE WANT TO GO OUT AND BUY SOMETHING FIT TO EAT, MR SCRAPE. COULD WE HAVE SOME OF THE POCKET-MONEY OUR PARENTS LEFT YOU TO GIVE OUT?

POCKET MONEY? DEAR ME, NO! YOU HAD FOUR PENCE THE YEAR BEFORE LAST! YOU MUST LEARN TO BE THRIFTY LIKE ME! AND NO SNEAKING OUT OF SCHOOL TODAY. YOU MUST DO ALL THE HOUSEWORK, AND THEN DO YOUR HOMEWORK.

NOTICE
NO SECOND HELPINGS OF ANYTHING SO DON'T ASK!

Scrape retired to his study to do his sums.

...88...89...OH, AND I MUSTN'T FORGET ALL THIS LOVELY LOLLY IN THE GIRLS' POCKET-MONEY ACCOUNT. IF THEY NEVER GET IT, THEY CAN'T WASTE IT—AND I CERTAINLY WON'T! TEE-HEE... 90...91...

CASH

Outside the headmaster's room—

HOUSEWORK, INDEED! WE'RE JUST UNPAID SERVANTS. TELL HIM WE'RE GOING ON STRIKE, POPPY!

RIGHT! BUT IT WON'T DO ANY GOOD!

HEADMASTER

Then Poppy joined the crowd at the door—

FUNNY LOOKING ½p. IT'S GOT GEORGE AND THE DRAGON ON THE BACK!

EEK! THERE MAY BE SOME MORE OF THOSE UNDER THE FLOORBOARDS. TO WORK, EBENEEZER! MONEY MUSTN'T LIE IDLE. HEE! HEE!

HEY! THAT'S AN OLD-FASHIONED GOLD SOVEREIGN! WORTH ABOUT £15 NOWADAYS, THAT IS. I'LL GIVE YOU A FIVER FOR IT!

CASH

AH! I SEE THEM! A WHOLE PILE OF NICE, ROUND THINGS. ALL GOLDEN COLOURED! I'LL BAG SOME OF THOSE!

Mr Scrape's greed made him careless, and—

YEEE-OW! BRASS DRAWING PINS! AND, BY THE WAY, WHERE'S MY CASH BOX?

IT'S ON THE OLD LUMBER MAN'S BARROW, SIR! WE THOUGHT YOU'D THROWN IT OUT AS OLD RUBBISH. IT DIDN'T LOOK WORTH MUCH!

HI! HI! HI! HALT! PUFF!

COME ON, GIRLS. WE'LL GO AND GET THAT SLAP-UP MEAL. OLD SCROOGE WILL NEVER KNOW WE'VE GONE!

Poppy hadn't sold her sovereign when she realised how much it was worth.

AS MUCH FOOD AS THIS GOLD SOVEREIGN WILL BUY, PLEASE.

THUMBS UP!

It's fun to see what you can draw using your thumb as a basic outline. This is a good way of amusing yourself on a long journey, while confined to bed, or even just for fun. All you need is a pencil and a little imagination!

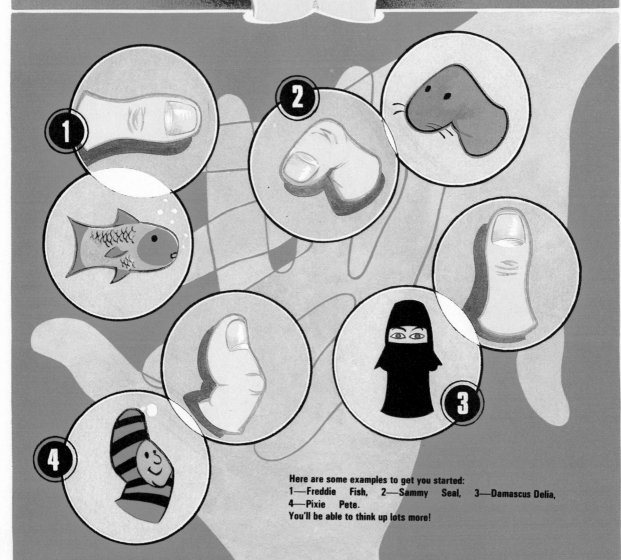

Here are some examples to get you started:
1—Freddie Fish, 2—Sammy Seal, 3—Damascus Delia,
4—Pixie Pete.
You'll be able to think up lots more!

BARNEY BEAR

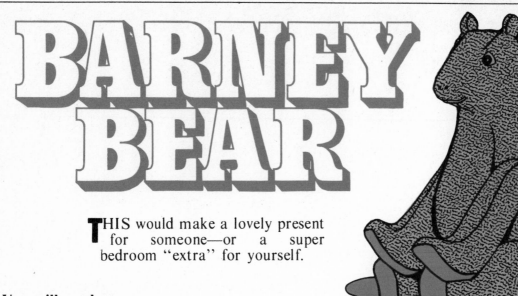

THIS would make a lovely present for someone—or a super bedroom "extra" for yourself.

You will need:
1 yd. brown fur fabric
¼ yd. yellow fur fabric
Foam or other stuffing
2 brown buttons
scraps of white felt for eyes
some red wool

TO MAKE THE PATTERN
Mark off a large sheet of paper into 1 in. squares.
Follow the diagrams of the pattern given and draw them accurately on the paper.
Ensure that you mark all the letters.
Now cut out your pattern pieces carefully.

TO CUT OUT
Smooth out the brown fur fabric and lay it flat, fur side down, on a smooth surface. Pin on all the pattern pieces except the front and hind paw pieces leaving ½ in. at least between the pattern pieces. Cut out each piece allowing ¼ in. all round for seams. Mark each piece at the letters with coloured threads; e.g. Mark all "A"s with blue thread, all "B"s with red thread, etc.

Cut out another side piece making sure it faces in the opposite direction to the piece already cut so that the two smooth sides are facing when you put them together.

Cut another hind leg piece and a front leg piece in the same way as the second side piece. Now cut another two pieces each face to face for the hind legs and the front legs but cutting on the lines E to H and K to O.

You will also need four ear pieces cut face to face.

Using the yellow fur fabric, pin the pattern pieces for the hind paw and the front paw to the material leaving ½ in. between the pieces. Cut out allowing ¼ in. for seams. Repeat and cut two more.

Remember to mark all letters with coloured thread.

TO MAKE UP
Take the two side pieces and pin them to the back piece, matching the coloured threads, with fur sides inside. Stitch up firmly. Join on the stomach piece and stitch firmly leaving an opening for the stuffing. Make up the ears; turn the body right side out and stitch the ears to the head.

To make the legs up, take one short front leg piece, one long front leg piece and one front paw piece. Pin all the side seams with fur inside, matching coloured threads. Stitch firmly. Make up the other three legs similarly.

Turn right sides out and fill firmly with stuffing. Stitch to the body where shown.

Cut out two circles of white felt and sew the two buttons to these for the eyes. Sew these firmly in place on the head.

Now stuff the body and close the bottom seam.

Sew on the nose and mouth with red wool.

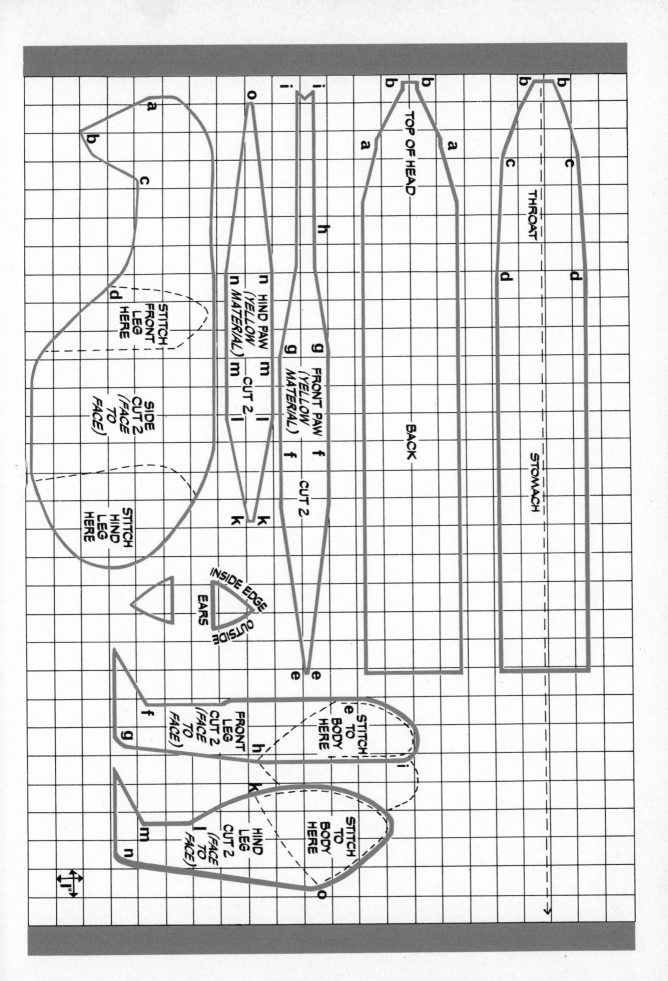

MAKE YOUR OWN POP-CORN!

1. BUY SOME DRIED MAIZE, PUT A TABLESPOON INTO A SAUCEPAN AND PUT ON MEDIUM HEAT WITH THE LID ON.

MAIZE

2. SHAKE THE PAN OCCASIONALLY TO PREVENT BURNING AND IN ABOUT FIVE MINUTES YOU'LL HEAR THE MAIZE POPPING. IF YOU USE A HEAT-PROOF GLASS PLATE OR DISH INSTEAD OF THE SAUCEPAN LID, YOU'LL BE ABLE TO SEE THE CORN POPPING! WHEN IT'S FINISHED POPPING, TIP OUT ONTO A PLATE TO COOL.

SNAP! POP!

SUGAR

3. MAKE THE SUGAR COATING BY PUTTING :-
   2 OZS. SUGAR.
   2 TEASPOONS VINEGAR.
   2 TABLESPOONS WATER
   INTO YOUR SAUCEPAN AND BRINGING SLOWLY TO THE BOIL.

4. WHEN THE MIXTURE BEGINS TO BUBBLE, TURN THE HEAT DOWN LOW AND SIMMER FOR TWELVE MINUTES. FINALLY, TIP THE POPPED CORN INTO THE MIXTURE AND STIR GENTLY. TIP BACK ONTO THE PLATE TO COOL, AND YOU'RE ALL SET FOR A FEAST!

YUMMY!

BOBBY DAZZLER

I'LL STAND YOU A FEED AT THE TUCKSHOP, BOBBY.

NEVER MIND ABOUT A STALE BUN WITH DON, BOBBY! LOOK WHAT I'VE BROUGHT YOU!

WHAT AN ENORMOUS BOX OF CHOCOLATES! I CAN'T TAKE THIS, MIKE! IT MUST HAVE COST YOU A FORTUNE!

TAKE IT, BOBBY! WELL, MUST BE OFF! ER—GOT WORK TO DO!

MIKE RUSHING OFF TO WORK? I DON'T BELIEVE IT!

YOU'RE RIGHT, DON, THE MIND BOGGLES!

The next morning, while Bobby was getting ready for school—

MIKE'S UP ALREADY! HE'S BEEN OUT SOMEWHERE! THIS GETS MORE MYSTERIOUS.

Later, in class—

MIKE'S NODDING OFF. EARLY RISING DOESN'T AGREE WITH HIM. I'D BETTER ROUSE HIM BEFORE OLD BEAKY SPOTS HIM.

Bobby gave Mike a nudge—

OW!

CRUMBS! HIS ELBOW SLIPPED!

THUMP!

ER—SORRY, SIR! I—ER—I SLIPPED!

WELL, HE'S AWAKE NOW, ANYWAY!

After school—

FLOWERS FOR MISS DAZZLER!

THERE'S A NOTE SIGNED BY MIKE!

To Bobby From Mike

HOPE YOU LIKE THE FLOWERS, BOBBY! CAN'T STOP!

MIKE, HANG ON! CRUMBS, YOU'RE ALWAYS COMING AND GOING!

WE'VE JUST HAD A WARNING FROM THE POLICE THAT THERE'S A SNEAK-THIEF OPERATING IN THE DISTRICT. HE'S BROKEN INTO SEVERAL LOCAL HOUSES IN DAYLIGHT. WARN THE REST OF THE FORM NOT TO LEAVE VALUABLES LYING ABOUT.

YES, SIR.

BOBBY, I DON'T LIKE TO SAY THIS, BUT MIKE'S BEEN ACTING PRETTY STRANGE LATELY...SNEAKING OFF ON HIS OWN, BUYING EXPENSIVE PRESENTS.

MIKE A THIEF? NO, THAT'S NOT POSSIBLE, DON!

ALL THE SAME, MIKE'S UP TO SOMETHING. I'M GOING TO FOLLOW HIM AND FIND OUT WHAT IT IS.

THEN I'M COMING WITH YOU.

THERE HE IS, GOING UP TO THAT HOUSE! IS HE CASING THE JOINT, DO YOU THINK?

YOU'VE BEEN WATCHING TOO MUCH TELEVISION, DON!

HE'S DELIVERING NEWSPAPERS!

SO THAT'S IT! MIKE'S GOT A PAPER ROUND TO MAKE MONEY TO BUY ME PRESENTS! ISN'T THAT NICE?

GET DOWN, DON! THERE'S A SNEAKY-LOOKING BLOKE WATCHING MIKE, TOO!

EH?

WHAT'S HE DOING?

HE'S TRYING TO FORCE THE WINDOW!

HEY, YOU!

BLIMEY!

CHECKING TO SEE IF THE PAPER'S BEEN COLLECTED, I'D GUESS. IF IT'S STILL IN THE DOOR, HE KNOWS THE HOUSE IS EMPTY. THIS LOOKS LIKE THE THIEF, DON.

The thief tried to make his escape across the front gardens—and met Mike, still delivering papers.

AAAH!

OOF!

GERROFF!

WHAT'S GOING ON?

HE'S A THIEF! NO, NOT THE ONE WHO'S YELLING! THE OTHER ONE!

WOW!

Later—

I SOON SETTLED THAT FELLOW! PERHAPS I'LL GET A REWARD, THEN I CAN BUY YOU A REAL PRESENT, BOBBY.

OH, BOY! MY HERO!

THE END

DINAH WANTS A DOG!

DINAH'S Dad didn't like dogs, but Dinah was determined to wear him down!

CAN YOU LOOK AFTER MY CHIHUAHUA FOR THE NIGHT, DINAH?

YES, THAT WOULD BE SMASHING!

CHEEKY THE CHIHUAHUA IS SO SMALL, DAD WON'T EVEN KNOW HE'S THERE.

THERE'S A COMFY BED FOR YOU, CHEEKY. NOW, KEEP QUIET AND DAD WILL BE NONE THE WISER.

Cheeky soon got bored, and decided to explore.

And minutes later—

MUM! DINAH! I'M HOME!

EEK! MY HAT'S COME TO LIFE! I-I'M SEEING THINGS.

I-I DON'T BELIEVE IT!

MUST GET MY SHOES OFF. I'VE BEEN WORKING TOO HARD!

YOU KNOW, DAD, I'VE BEEN THINKING, A LITTLE CHIHUAHUA WOULDN'T BE ANY TROUBLE AT ALL!

A WHAT?

NOW MY SLIPPERS HAVE VANISHED!

MEET CHEEKY—HE'S MY FRIEND'S. I WANT ONE JUST LIKE HIM. AFTER ALL, IT'S A SMALL REQUEST!

IT WOULD DRIVE ME CRAZY—LITTLE BY LITTLE!

Next morning—

SO YOU'RE NOT BIG ENOUGH TO SHARE YOUR HOME WITH A TINY DOG, EH?

THAT'S ABOUT THE SIZE OF IT! OUT!

NUMBERS IN THE SAND

"The sands foretell all," chant the Arab fortune tellers of the Middle East. Once he has obtained a tourist customer, the Wise One asks him some questions and scratches in the sand with a piece of stick. Then he gives his customer a character analysis and makes forecasts about the client's chances of future happiness.

Here's how you, too, can tell fortunes using a method based on the Arab system. This method, known as Significant Numerology, is popular all over the world. Try it on your friends—just for fun.

1—Ask your friend to state her date of birth in numbers, and write it down. For example—5.11.1964.

2—Add the numbers together—in this case 5+11+1+9+6+4 = 36.

3—When the total comes to a number higher than 9, as it does in our example, add the digits together. So, 3+6 = 9, and that figure gives us our Sector Number. Now, give the personal summary shown in the list of Sector Readings.

NOTE—If the figure exceeds 9 even after adding the digits, simply add the digits once more. For instance, if your grandfather, let's say, was born on 6.2.1910 this adds up to 19. Adding 1 and 9 produces 10, so go one step further and add 1 + 0 = 1, therefore 1 is his Sector Number.

Sector Readings

1—Although you are perhaps not always imaginative, you make up for this with your abundant common-sense. Since you take life fairly seriously, you usually work more steadily and conscientiously than most. You are not simply a thought-less plodder, though; you frequently have flashes of brilliant inspiration that will help you to succeed in life at anything you choose to do.

2—Your strong points are your instinctive good judgment and ability to keep calm in emergencies. You seldom speak without thinking, and usually consider the consequences before taking action—both of which help to keep you out of trouble. You have a keen appreciation of life and beauty but sometimes tend to be mean with yourself, although not with others. Don't overdo economy!

3—Your temperament makes you a strange mixture. Sometimes you are friendly and charming, at other times you make people feel unwelcome and unwanted. This intrigues people and often makes you more sought-after than ever! It will do you good to have a steady, placid friend to turn to for advice. Try not to show your feelings so plainly.

4—It takes a lot to discourage you! You have the same spirit as the pioneers who opened up Africa and the American West. You may be stubborn at times, but your pluck, honesty and unselfishness ensure that you will never lack admiring friends. Take care that your breezy attitude doesn't frighten off shy acquaintances.

5—Being fond of comfort yourself, you are very hospitable and attentive to the needs of your friends. Although quick to anger, you are equally quick to forgive. Beware of being too trust-ing; some less scrupulous people may think it is weakness and try to take advantage of you.

6—You are inclined to be a person of fixed ideas, to the extent that you sometimes "bury your head in the sand" and pretend that unpleasant events and people do not really exist. Your choice of companions often amazes your parents and those who know you best. However, you have a happy knack of making the best of things and no one can say you lack intelligence.

7—You have been blessed with the soul of an artist combined with an enthusiastic outlook. You have plenty of imagination and real flair for the use of colour in clothes, decor and design. In keeping with artistic tradition, however, you may sometimes be moody, as your friends probably know. Do your best to keep cool when things try your patience.

8—Being shrewd in the choice of your friends is just one of the reasons that you are speedily successful in the things you attempt. The burning ambition, which drives you on while others falter, also helps. Your pride in yourself is understandable—just guard against being self-important in your manner.

9—Success doesn't often come easily for you, but you've got a dogged determination that will enable you to win through despite difficulties and disappointments. You often take things too much to heart, with the result that you are elated one day and dejected the next. Do try to keep a sense of proportion—things are seldom as black or white as they look to you! Apart from spells of day-dreaming, you are energetic, and your honesty and loyalty gain you many friends.

5
11
1
9
6
4
=36
=9

MY SERGEANT-MAJOR DAD

JENNY PETERS' father, a Sergeant-Major in the Royal Engineers, was a stickler for tidiness and punctuality—which Jenny was not. So when Sergeant-Major Peters came home on leave, trouble was brewing!

YOUR ROOM'S A MESS, JENNY! CLEAN IT UP!

I'LL DO IT LATER, DAD, ONCE THIS LP'S FINISHED.

YOU'LL DO IT NOW, YOUNG LADY!

OH, IT'S ROTTEN, DAD BEING HOME AGAIN! I WISH HE'D STAYED OUT IN HONG KONG WITH HIS REGIMENT! DO THIS—CLEAN UP THAT! WHY DO I HAVE TO HAVE A SERGEANT-MAJOR DAD?

MUM AND THE KIDS LOVE HAVING HIM HOME. BUT WHY MUST HE ACT THE WAY HE DOES?

ALL RIGHT, ALL RIGHT, YER ON TEA PARADE. LEMME SEE IF THEM HANDS ARE ALL NICE AN' SHINY!

TWENTY-FOUR FINGERS, SIX THUMBS, ALL PRESENT AND CORRECT, SUH!

YES, YOU'VE GOT A NICE FAMILY, MRS PETERS. YOU'VE DONE WELL OVER THE MONTHS I'VE BEEN AWAY—THOUGH I THINK MAYBE ONE OF THEM TENDS TO BE A LITTLE BIT SLACK.

OH, I WISH THEY'D SEND HIM BACK TO HONG KONG.

Tea over, Jenny made her usual dash to get out—

HOW ABOUT HELPING MUM WITH THE WASHING-UP, JENNY, BEFORE YOU PUSH OFF?

BUT IT'S YOUTH CLUB NIGHT. I DON'T WANT TO BE LATE.

DON'T ARGUE! GET IT DONE!

In the kitchen—

SLOPPY, GIRL—SLOPPY! IF YOU WERE IN THE ARMY YOU'D BE IN TROUBLE.

BUT I'M NOT IN YOUR ROTTEN OLD ARMY, AM I? AND I DON'T THINK I'M EVER LIKELY TO BE.

At the club—

HI, THERE—YOU LOOK LIKE SOMEBODY'S JUST MELTED YOUR RECORDS. YOU GOT TROUBLES?

IT'S ALMOST AS BAD. MY SERGEANT-MAJOR DAD'S HOME AND IT'S LIKE LIVING IN A BARRACKS!

Jenny had admired Greg for a long time—but he'd never shown any interest in her before.

WELL, NOT TO WORRY. HE ISN'T AROUND NOW, IS HE? COME ON, LET'S GO THROUGH TO THE DISCO DANCE AND HAVE A BALL. IT'S ABOUT TO START.

YOU...YOU MEAN YOU AND ME?

At the disco—

GOSH, I NEVER THOUGHT HE'D EVER NOTICE ME. I'VE WANTED THIS TO HAPPEN FOR AGES.

Greg introduced Jenny to his friends—

FOLKS, MEET JENNY PETERS. I'VE JUST ASKED TO TAKE HER HOME AND SHE'S SAID YES.

HOW'S IT GOING, THEN?

HI, JENNY!

HELLO, EVERYBODY.

Outside the house—

TIME TO COME IN!

G...GOLLY!

G...GOODNIGHT, GREG. I'VE GOT TO GO.

AT THE DOUBLE!

YEH, AND IT SOUNDS LIKE HE WANTS TO GIVE YOU SOME DRILL!

A lecture followed—

DID YOU HAVE TO SHOUT LIKE THAT? YOU'VE REALLY MADE ME LOOK SMALL!

WHEN I TELL YOU TO BE IN AT TWENTY-TWO THIRTY HOURS I MEAN IT, JENNY—NOT TEN MINUTES LATER...

...ALSO, YOUR ROOM IS SUCH A SHAMBLES I'VE DECIDED TO INSPECT IT EVERY DAY. I WANT TO FIND IT TIDY. RIGHT?

YES, SERGEANT-MAJOR.

Several nights later at the youth club—

LEFT, RIGHT, LEFT, RIGHT, PICK 'EM UP THERE, PRIVATE PETERS!

IMAGINE HAVING TO BE IN BY HALF-PAST TEN!

STOP IT! LEAVE ME ALONE!

IT ISN'T FAIR! GREG'S TOLD EVERYBODY WHAT HAPPENED AND NOW I'M A LAUGHING STOCK.

CARLY SIMON

growing up

CARLY SIMON was born and brought up in Martha's Vineyard, near Boston, Massachusetts. From an early age, she sang because it came naturally and because she enjoyed it!

But Carly's first ambition wasn't to be a singer—she really wanted to be a spy!

WHAT ON EARTH IS THAT CHILD DOING, SLINKING ALONG LIKE THAT?

MOST UNSUITABLE—NOT AT ALL LADYLIKE!

Carly was so shy at school that, when she won a prize, she trembled so much she could hardly get on to the platform to collect it!

I—I CAN'T GO ON...ALL THOSE PEOPLE...

SURE YOU CAN, CARLY—WINNING THE MUSIC PRIZE IS SOMETHING TO BE PROUD OF!

Even today, Carly still suffers from nerves before a public appearance.

Carly went on to the Sarah Lawrence College and had music lessons from folk singer Pete Seeger, in Greenwich Village.

WE'LL TRY THAT CHORUS AGAIN, CARLY, AND THIS TIME YOU PLAY THE ACCOMPANIMENT.

GREAT! I JUST LOVE THIS SONG!

Carly followed up her interest in singing by forming a double act with her sister, Lucy.

THESE GIRLS ARE GOOD!

YES, THEY SHOULD BE VERY POPULAR.

The girls WERE popular, until Lucy got married and the duo broke up.

Then Carly met Albert Grossman, manager of top stars like Bob Dylan.

CARLY, YOU'LL BE A SUPERSTAR!

I SURE HOPE YOU'RE RIGHT—THINGS HAVE FALLEN FLAT FOR ME SINCE LUCY LEFT.

In 1966, Carly made a record, but unfortunately, it was never released.

But Carly made friends with David Bromberg, who introduced her to a big record company. Early in 1971 she made her first album, "Carly Simon".

WELL, IT HASN'T EXACTLY STORMED THE CHARTS, BUT IT'S A START, AND MAYBE NEXT TIME...

Meanwhile, Carly was making a name for herself at college concerts and folk clubs. She was chosen as supporting singer to Cat Stevens at the Troubadour Club in Los Angeles.

SINGING WITH CAT HAS BEEN GREAT EXPERIENCE FOR ME.

Cat Stevens' producer helped Carly with her second album, which contained a lot of her own songs—and this time she had a hit!

"ANTICIPATION" A HIT FOR CARLY

WORLD CLASS SONGS ON SECOND SIMON ALBUM

Also in 1971, Cat introduced Carly to James Taylor, well-known already as a singer and songwriter.

HI! HAVEN'T WE MET BEFORE?

YES— I WAS BROUGHT UP IN MARTHA'S VINEYARD, TOO. WE MUST HAVE BEEN NEIGHBOURS WHEN WE WERE CHILDREN!

James and Carly hit it off right away and, before long, James proposed—in London's Oxford Street!

WILL YOU MARRY ME, CARLY?

OH, JAMES—I'D LOVE TO!

Carly and James bought a house in Martha's Vineyard and Carly did a lot of the decorating herself—with some help from her dog!

OH, NO! LOOK AT THE MESS YOU'VE MADE, YOU RASCAL!

When, at last, they were able to move into their own home—

JAMES! DO YOU REALISE THAT BETWEEN US WE'VE GOT TEN GUITARS?

GOOD JOB WE BOUGHT A BIG HOUSE, OR THERE'D BE NO ROOM FOR THEM ALL!

But meanwhile, Carly was having trouble with her forthcoming single—the one that was to take her to the top of the charts all over the world!

SORRY, FOLKS—WE'LL HAVE TO TAKE A BREAK AND THEN TRY IT AGAIN.

THAT'S ABOUT FIFTY TAKES FOR ONE LITTLE SONG! IT MUST HAVE A JINX ON IT!

But there was no jinx on "You're So Vain". It rocked the pop world and Carly was pestered to reveal the identity of "Mr Vanity"—but apart from denying it was James Taylor, she kept her secret!

Carly's third album, "No Secrets", featured an all-star cast backing.

MICK JAGGER

DORIS TROY

JAMES TAYLOR

PAUL AND LINDA McCARTNEY

During his recent American tour, James was joined by Carly for some of the time and critics were calling them "The King and Queen of the Seventies".

" THAT'S THE WAY I'VE ALWAYS HEARD IT SHOULD BE...."

With dozens of beautiful songs to her credit, Carly Simon can now relax and enjoy her success. She's right at the top and likely to stay there.

A DISC DATE WITH

START 20

19

18
DISC DOING BADLY
MISS A TURN

17

16
HOLD-UP IN DISC SUPPLIES
GO BACK TO 19

15
IF YOU ARRIVED HERE IN ONE GO FROM THE START—
DISC DOING WELL.
MOVE TO 14

14

13
AN UNLUCKY SPOT IN THE CHARTS
MISS A TURN

12

SLUMP

SLUMP

SLUMP

Imagine that you've made your first disc. Now, watch it move up the top twenty chart.

Thrills galore as you achieve your ambition to make a disc with Donny!
See overleaf for full instructions.

HOORAY!
YOU'VE MADE IT.! YOU MAKE A SMASH HIT DISC WITH DONNY AND YOU'VE WON THE GAME!

TO COMPLETE YOUR DISC GAME —

Place a sheet of card under this page to avoid cutting the following page, then, using a sharp knife and a straight-edge, carefully make the cuts shown. Lightly score the dotted lines.

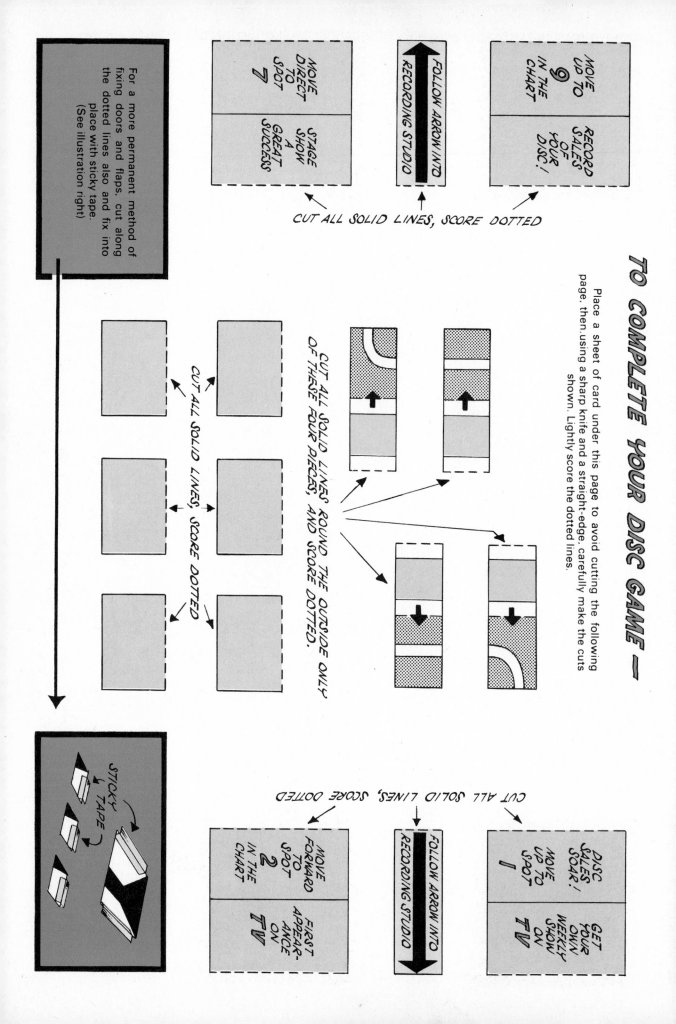

MOVE UP TO 6 IN THE CHART

RECORD SALES OF YOUR DISC!

FOLLOW ARROW INTO RECORDING STUDIO

MOVE DIRECT TO SPOT 7

STAGE SHOW A GREAT SUCCESS

CUT ALL SOLID LINES, SCORE DOTTED

For a more permanent method of fixing doors and flaps, cut along the dotted lines also and fix into place with sticky tape. (See illustration right)

CUT ALL SOLID LINES ROUND THE OUTSIDE ONLY OF THESE FOUR PIECES, AND SCORE DOTTED.

CUT ALL SOLID LINES, SCORE DOTTED

STICKY TAPE

CUT ALL SOLID LINES, SCORE DOTTED

DISC SALES SOAR! MOVE UP TO SPOT 1

GET YOUR OWN WEEKLY SHOW ON TV

FOLLOW ARROW INTO RECORDING STUDIO

MOVE FORWARD TO SPOT 2 IN THE CHART

FIRST APPEAR-ANCE ON TV

TO PLAY DISC DATE

1—You need a dice, and a counter for each player. Throw in turn and move round the board, carrying out the instructions. When you land on a door or flap, remain there until your next turn before following the instructions. **2**—If you arrive in a SLUMP column, move downwards, counting one for each space. **3**—When you get to the JUKE-BOX, throw the dice to see which box to land on.—e.g. if you throw a '2' place your counter on No. 2 flap, then wait till your next turn to open it and discover the name of your hit single—'Don't Ask My Name'. Then move your counter forward one space for each word in the song title—in this case, there are four words so you finish on Spot 3 in the chart. **4**—If you are unfortunate enough to pay a visit to the RECORDING STUDIO to re-make your disc, move your counter round, in the direction of the white arrow, and according to your dice throw.

CONTINUED ➤

YES! YOU'RE REALLY IN A FLAP!

When you finish up on a 'Flap', open it right across and move your counter to the other half of the 'Recording Studio' in the direction of the small black arrow, like this

DON'T ASK MY NAME	IT'S A SIN TO LIE
	ROSES ARE FOREVER
ONLY YOU	SMILES AND TEARS MUST GO TOGETHER
ALWAYS	

6—If you land on a 'Studio' flap already opened, do not fold it back again. Close all four flaps after going to the 'Juke-Box'.

Only one player can be in the 'Studio' at a time. Others must queue up until the flaps are closed.

If one player is in the 'Studio' and the rest are ALL queueing, then the player in the 'Studio' may open all flaps immediately and proceed direct to the 'Juke-Box'.

5—On your next turn, continue round the new half of the 'Studio' until you can open another flap in the same way. You will eventually open all four flaps, revealing a broad arrow. Proceed down this into the 'Juke-Box'.

STUDIO

FLAP OPEN

RECORDING

YOUR TYPE OF MUSIC GOING OUT OF FAVOUR!

PATCHWORK PEG

Here is a simple little peg-doll that can be made up from bits and pieces. You will need:-

1 clothes-peg	lid from used aerosol	some wool	scraps of material
2 pipecleaners	needle and thread	felt pens	glue
sticky tape	flexible card	paper doily	cotton-wool

1 Place the pipe cleaner in the peg as shown.

2 Fold the "arms" up and wrap sticky tape round to hold them in place. Bend "arms" down.

3 Cut two pieces of material slightly less than the length of the "arm" and 1 inch wide. Glue, then wind round "arms"

4 Glue the cotton-wool onto the peg for the "chest". Cut a piece of material long enough to go round the "chest" twice leaving 1½ inches clear at the foot. Glue the "bodice" to the peg finishing at at the back of the doll.

5 Glue the "head" (but not the "face") and, using strands of wool, starting at the back of the doll, stick on the hair.

6 FRONT VIEW. Bring the wool forward and stick to the front of the "head."

7 BACK VIEW. Reverse and cover the "bald patch" with the ends. When the glue has dried, trim the ends.

8 Draw on the face with felt pens.

9 TOPSIDE. UNDERSIDE. 6½". Cut a circle of material 6½ inches in diameter and either iron on stiffening or glue to a circle of flexible card. Mark the stiffening into 8 equal sections. Decorate the edge of the topside with a piece of braid, lace or the edge of a paper doily.

10 Cut a hole slightly less than the size of the peg for a tight fit and push the peg into the "skirt".

11 Make a hole, the size of the peg, in the centre of the aerosol lid for the stand. Push the peg in to the stand.

12 With a needle and thread make a tiny stitch at the foot of each pencil mark, leaving 6 inches of thread at start and finish.

13 Pull the thread until the "skirt" pleats neatly. Tidy off the ends.

14 HAT. TOP. Cut a circle 1¾ inches across and cut a smaller circle out of the centre. Keep this disc. Cut a thin strip for the hat band. Glue.

15 UMBRELLA. PIPE CLEANER. FRILL. Bend a pipe cleaner as shown. Cut a piece of material as shown and stiffen it as in 9. Glue the material into a cone shape with the hole small enough to fit the pipe cleaner.

That's the easiest way to make our peg-doll. Once you've made a few, try experimenting with cuffs and puff sleeves, trimmings, etc. Good luck.

HANDLE WITH CARE

If you have a pet, you should know how to handle it properly. Remember all pets, large and small, are living creatures and should be treated gently. Handle them as lightly as possible and do not squeeze.

LARGE DOGS
Only lift a large dog if it needs lifting and never try to lift a strange dog, large or small. Bend down and put one arm beneath the dog's stomach, putting the other arm under the neck and clasp your hands together. Carry the dog by holding it close to your body.

SMALL DOGS AND CATS
Support the hind legs with your right hand and the front legs with your left hand, with the 1st finger between the paws.

CATS
If you have to carry your cat a long distance this method is advisable. Using your right hand, place the index finger between the front legs, supporting the cat's right leg with your thumb and index finger and its left with the other fingers. Tuck the cat under your arm, supporting its back legs gently but firmly with the elbow.

HAMSTERS AND GERBILS
These two animals are handled in the same way. Support the animal in the palm of your hand and place the 2nd, 3rd and 4th fingers of your right hand lightly round the chest with the 1st finger and thumb lightly round the neck to prevent it biting. Never lift or hold a gerbil by the tail.

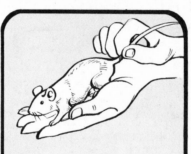

MICE
Hold a mouse lightly by the middle of its tail, supporting the body in the palm of the other hand. Do not hold on for too long and always be gentle.

GUINEA-PIGS
"Sit" the guinea-pig in your right hand and support its chest and front legs with your left hand.

BUDGERIGARS
A budgerigar will perch on your finger quite happily if tame. If you want to lift the bird to put it back in its cage, hold it from behind, ensuring the wings are folded close to its body, allowing its legs to hang free between your fingers.

RABBITS
Never pick up a rabbit by the ears. Support its hind-quarters with one hand and its chest with the other, holding its front legs lightly between your fingers.

If you handle your pets properly they will not attempt to bite or scratch you. Always remember with animals that you must handle with care.

BIG SPENDER

BIG LIZ SPENDER was Summerfield School's most amazing girl athlete—unless she happened to get a crush on some boy. Then Liz's incredible performance would go completely to pieces and force sports captain, Jean Craig, to adopt desperate 'cures'.

One day, Liz was training for the County Championships.

JUST LOOK AT BIG LIZ GO! WOW!

Jean was with sports mistress, Miss Steel.

INCREDIBLE! SHE'S ALREADY INSIDE THE COUNTY RECORD.

WE'RE A CERT FOR THE CHAMPIONSHIP ON THE BIG DAY!

WHAT A PITY THERE WERE NO BOYS TO WATCH ME. OF COURSE, THEY PROBABLY EXPECT I DO BALLET.

SHE'S GOT TO BE KIDDING!

SSH! LIZ THINKS SHE'S THE DISHIEST FEMALE SINCE CLEOPATRA!

ROMANTIC?

They started for home.

BOYS—THAT'S OUR WORRY! WE HAVE TO KEEP LIZ CLEAR OF A CRUSH BEFORE THE CHAMPIONSHIP.

ARE YOU WHISPERING ABOUT ATHLETICS? ANYONE. BUT ANYONE. CAN RUN FAST. NOW, IF I WERE IN 'SWAN LAKE'...

Suddenly—

HEY, LOOK OUT!

OH, NO!

LISTEN, LIZ—

DON'T BUG ME. I'VE A FISHING DATE WITH PAUL. MMM, HE'S SO DREAMY!

LIZ, ABOUT THE COUNTY CHAMPIONSHIP...

WHAT ABOUT IT? RUN IT YOURSELF! NOW LEAVE ME IN PEACE!

Later, at home—

I'VE GOT TO CURE HER! I MUST! BUT HOW?

I'VE GOT IT!

At the river—

THAT'S IT—YOU'RE GETTING THE IDEA, LIZ.

OH, PAUL, YOU'RE SO MASTERFUL AND STRONG.

At the County meeting—

LOVELY TO LOOK AT

Perhaps we can't all be lovely to look at, but we can make the best of what we have by taking proper care of our skin, hair and appearance.

Face Facts

If you want nice skin, you must first discover what type it is, then treat it accordingly. Apart from a normal skin, there are three main types—dry, greasy and combination skin, which, as the name implies, is a mixture of a dry and greasy skin.

GREASY SKIN . . .

This is shiny and more prone to spots and blackheads than the other skin types. If you have greasy skin, cleansing and toning is of vital importance in helping to prevent blemishes. After washing, use a toner liberally to close the pores and thus protect the skin from excess grease.

Even greasy skins need a little moisture at some point, but it's best to use only a little of the lightest, non-greasy creams or lotions.

DRY SKIN . . .

This flakes in extreme weather conditions, feels tight in the mornings or after washing and is usually pale in colour. If you have this skin type, it's best to use a cream cleanser rather than soap and water as this is always drying. There are several good, inexpensive cream cleansers on the market for you to choose from.

A toner or astringent is a good thing to use on normal, greasy and combination skins, but when used on a dry skin, it only increases the dryness. The right amount of toning for dry skin, however, can be achieved by splashing the face with cold water after cleansing. Nourishing skin—especially a dry skin—is an important point. Use a moisturiser when you go out, at night, and in the morning. Again there are plenty of inexpensive moisturisers available.

If dry skin is continually flaking and sore, despite proper care and attention, it may be your diet that's at fault. Try eating lots of high-protein foods like eggs, milk and cheese.

COMBINATION SKIN . . .

This is a greasy panel across the forehead, down the nose and chin, with dry or normal skin on cheeks. If this is your skin type, cleanse in the usual way, then treat the greasy patches with toner and the dry bits with moisturiser.

SPOTS . . .

are everyone's problem at some time or another! If you are particularly prone to spots, it's wise to use an antiseptic soap and to take extra time over cleansing and toning affected areas. If you wear make-up, use a medicated brand; and if you don't wear make-up, cover spots with a special concealing stick until they clear up.

Hair Care

A girl's hair is her crowning glory—or it should be! Here are a few tips on how you can keep your hair shiny and healthy.

As with skin, there are several hair types—dry, greasy, normal and problem —'problem' including hair with excess dandruff, hair that continually looks dull and lifeless, or difficult, unmanageable hair. Now-adays, there's a wide range of shampoos for you to choose from, so it's easy to find a shampoo that's right for your own particular type of hair. Using a variety of shampoos, even for the same hair type, won't do your hair any good, though, so try to stick to the one you like best.

Wash your hair as often as is needed and get into the habit of brushing it before you wash it as this removes dust particles from the hair, making it easier to wash and consequently giving it an even cleaner and shinier

look. Make sure all the shampoo has been rinsed off, otherwise scalp irritation may result and your hair may take on a lank, unattractive look.

Visit a hairdresser regularly to keep your hair neat and tidy. Don't be tempted to ask a friend to 'tidy it up' or to do it yourself as this can result in disaster! Elastic bands ruin hair, so don't use them, and never backcomb as this splits hair, making it look unsightly. Finally, that old belief that brushing your hair a hundred times per night enhances it is not true! Severe and continual brushing only activates the oil glands in the scalp making them produce more oil and therefore making the hair greasy. However, if your hair is very dry, then a lot of brushing can take away some of the dryness.

If you follow all these basic rules, you can be satisfied that you're making the best of your appearance. But, remember, girls, there's a lot of truth in the saying that beauty is only skin deep. You don't have to be pretty to be attractive. A happy personality can make a plain girl just as attractive as a pretty girl—sometimes more so!

Christmas Spread

SHORTBREAD

INGREDIENTS:

4OZ. FLOUR
2OZ. RICE FLOUR
4OZ. MARGARINE
2OZ. CASTER SUGAR

Method:

Sieve flour, rice flour and sugar into a bowl. Add margarine and work ingredients together into a ball. Shape into a round cake and bake at 350°F. or Gas Mark 3 for 30-40 minutes until it begins to colour.

CHRISTMAS CAKE

Ingredients:
8 oz. plain flour
1 teaspoonful baking powder
1 teaspoonful mixed spice
Pinch of salt
6 oz. softened butter
6 oz. caster sugar
3 lightly beaten eggs
2 oz. raisins
2 oz. glacé cherries
8 oz. sultanas
8 oz. currants
Approx. 4 tablespoonsful milk to mix

METHOD:

Sieve flour, baking powder, mixed spice and salt into a bowl. Weigh fruit, and mix together in another bowl. In another large bowl, cream butter and sugar thoroughly, then gradually beat in the eggs a little at a time. Stir in the fruit. Fold in the flour mixture alternating with the milk, finishing with a little flour.

Turn mixture into a lined 8 in. or 9 in. diameter cake tin. Bake in the centre of the oven, for two and a half hours at 300°F. or Gas Mark 2.

Allow to cool in the tin, then store in an airtight container in a cool place. Decorate as you wish.

MINCE PIES

You can make these with bought mincemeat, but why not make your own?

MINCEMEAT INGREDIENTS:

2 oz. raisins
1½ oz. mixed peel
2 oz. cooking apples
½ oz. blanched almonds
1½ oz. shredded suet
2 oz. moist brown sugar
2 oz. currants
grated rind and juice of ½ lemon
¼ teaspoonful mixed spice
2 teaspoonsful brandy (ask Mum to give you this.)

METHOD:

Finely chop the raisins, mixed peel, almonds and apples.
Mix thoroughly with the other ingredients.
Leave overnight.

SHORTCRUST PASTRY

Ingredients:

8 oz. flour
2 oz. margarine
2 oz. lard
pinch of salt
2 tablespoonsful cold water

Sieve flour and salt then rub in margarine and lard until mixture resembles fine breadcrumbs. Using a knife at first, then fingertips, add water until the dough is suitable for rolling. When rolling it out, lift and turn the pastry to keep it light.

TO MAKE THE MINCE PIES

Roll the pastry to just under ¼ in. thick.
Cut out twelve rounds to fit patty tins. Roll out trimmings and cut out 12 rounds slightly larger than patty tins. Line greased patty tins with the larger rounds.
Divide the mincemeat equally into 12 tins. Dampen edges with milk or beaten egg, and seal on pastry lids, making two small slits in each lid.
Bake at 425°F. or Gas Mark 6 for 20-25 mins.
While still hot, dredge with caster sugar.

SIMPLE TRIFLE

Ingredients:

1 packet trifle sponges
1 packet jelly
1 tin fruit
  (sliced peaches are ideal)
1 pint custard
Tinned or fresh cream
Flaked chocolate OR
  cake decoration
  of your choice

METHOD:

Drain the fruit but keep the syrup. Place the trifle sponges in a large dish and soak with syrup from the fruit. Make up the jelly according to the instructions on the packet, putting any excess syrup in the jelly.

Pour the jelly when cool, but not setting, over the sponges, and put aside to set.

When the jelly is set, arrange the sliced peaches carefully on top. Make the custard, and when it has cooled pour gently over to cover the peaches.

About an hour before serving, whip up the cream, spread over set custard and sprinkle with flaked chocolate, chocolate vermicelli or sugar strands, etc.

How to make simple things Christmassy

If you don't like heavy fruit cake with marzipan, why not try some of the following ideas to make some simple cakes and biscuits with a festive flavour?

1—Ice an ordinary sandwich sponge cake. When the icing is set, paint on a Christmas scene with vegetable dyes.

2—Arrange silver and coloured ball cake decorations in a Christmas shape, e.g. fir tree, Father Christmas, snowman, etc.

3—Using either a bought or a home-made Swiss roll, make a yule log cake by covering it with melted chocolate which you "roughen" with the back of a spoon as it begins to harden. When the chocolate has set, place some icing to look like snow on the chocolate, and stick a piece of imitation holly on the icing.

4—Make up shortbread or any biscuit mixture and cut with various shaped cutters. Again ice and decorate with vegetable dyes or cake decorations.

WAWA, N. ONTARIO, CANADA.
Glenda Bruce, Cardiff.

HORSESHOE FALLS, CANADA.
Allison Shaw, Warrington.

MOUNT RUSHMORE, U.S.A.
Jo Ross, Woking.

BUCKINGHAM PALACE, LONDON.
Fiona Thomson, London.

DUTCH DRESS, NETHERLANDS.
Karen Barrett, Glenrothes.

AUDIERNE, FRANCE.
Christine Taylor, Derby.

EIGER, SWITZERLAND.
Maureen Jamieson, Sale.

LAS RAMBLAS, BARCELONA.
Margaret Gibson, Wick.

EDINBURGH ZOO, SCOTLAND.
Anne Duncan, Manchester.

HAARLEM, NETHERLANDS.
Morna McIntosh, Newcastle.

UTRECHT, NETHERLANDS.
Marion Yule, Oxford.